MARYLAND
MSA
NEW EDITION

Coach
America's Best for Student Success

Mathematics

GRADE
8

Jerome D. Kaplan, Ed.D.
Professor Emeritus
Seton Hall University

MSA Coach, Mathematics, New Edition, Grade 8
99MD
1-59823-303-3

EVP, Publisher: Bill Scroggie
VP, Editorial Director: Marie Spano
VP of Production: Dina Goren
Art Director: Farzana Razak

Senior Development Editor: Cindy Walter
Development Editor: Amy Goodale
Author: Jerome D. Kaplan, Ed. D.
Layout Artist: Ken Weisner
Cover Design: Farzana Razak
Cover Photo: Onne van der Wal / Corbis

Triumph Learning® 136 Madison Avenue, 7th Floor, New York, NY 10016
© 2007 Triumph Learning, LLC
A Haights Cross Communications, Inc. company

Printed in the United States of America.

10 9 8 7 6 5 4 3 2 1

Table of Contents

3

To the Student

This book is called a *Coach*. It will help you prepare for the Grade 8 MSA Math Test.

Here is how the *Coach* can help you:

- It shows you what math questions on the MSA Test are like.

- It tells you what you need to know to do well on the test.

- Finally, it gives you practice on the kind of math that will be on the test.

The MSA Test in Math has many **Selected Response (SR)** questions. They are like the ones you will work with in this book. After each question there are four possible answers. Only one is correct. The others are wrong. You must mark the one correct answer after each question.

The MSA Test also has **Brief Constructed Response (BCR)** questions. On these questions, you will have to write the answer (Step A) and then write a short explanation of why your answer is correct (Step B).

The MSA test has **Extended Constructed Response (ECR)** questions. These multi-step questions ask you to provide an answer and to show and explain your work.

The MSA Test also has **Student Produced Response (SPR)** items. In these items, you will find your answer and then shade in the bubbles on a grid that correspond to your answer.

Here are some tips that will help when you work in this book and take the test:

- Read each question carefully.

- Work as carefully as you can.

- Make sure you answer the question that is asked.

- Ask yourself if the answer makes sense.

- Answer as many questions as you can.

- On selected response questions, if you cannot decide on the answer, make the best guess you can. There is no penalty for guessing.

- On constructed-response questions, make sure you write a clear explanation for Step B.

Use these tips throughout the book and when you take the test.

You need to be able to read and write numbers into the millions.

Algebra, Patterns, or Functions

In this unit, you will learn about number patterns and algebra. You will learn to identify equivalent equations—equations that have the same solution.

Try This

You will need:

- two groups of 2 people
- pencil and paper
- a watch or clock
- 8 pieces of paper with the numbers 1–3 and 5–9
- a small bag or box

Follow these steps:

1. Study these four equations:

    $$n + 5 = 9 \qquad n - 1 = 3 \qquad 5n = 20 \qquad n \div 2 = 2$$

    You can use mental math to solve these one-step equations to see that they all have the same solution, 4. Equations that have the same solution are equivalent equations.

2. Place the numbered pieces of paper in the bag. A person from each pair draws one number from the bag. Appoint one person in the group to be timekeeper. When the timekeeper says "start," each pair has 2 minutes to work together to write as many equations as possible that have the number on the paper as a solution.

3. Each pair's set of equations must include at least one addition equation, one subtraction equation, one multiplication equation, and one division equation.

4. When time is up, pairs trade equation sets to check the work. The pair with more correct equations wins the round.

5. Play more rounds without returning the numbered pieces of paper to the bag.

Think about it:

What can you do to both sides of the equation $n = 4$ to create an addition equation? a subtraction equation? a multiplication equation? a division equation?

LESSON

1 Extending Patterns

Two kinds of number patterns are arithmetic (pronounced ar-ith-me-*tic*) sequences and geometric sequences.

In an arithmetic sequence, there is a common difference between the terms.

Example 1

This is an arithmetic sequence:

4, 11, 18, 25, 32, 39,...

1) Find the common difference.

2) Find the eighth term of the sequence.

STRATEGY: Subtract consecutive terms. Then extend the sequence to the eighth term.

STEP 1: Find the common difference.

Subtract consecutive terms:

$11 - 4 = 7$

$18 - 11 = 7$

$25 - 18 = 7$

$32 - 25 = 7$

$39 - 32 = 7$

STEP 2: Extend the sequence by adding the common difference.

There are six given terms. The sixth term is 39.

So, $39 + 7 = 46$, the seventh term

$46 + 7 = 53$, the eighth term

SOLUTION: The common difference is 7, and the eighth term is 53.

In a geometric sequence, there is a common ratio between the terms.

Example 2

This is a geometric sequence:

2, 6, 18, 54,…

1) Find the common ratio.

2) Find the eighth term of the sequence.

STRATEGY: **Divide consecutive terms. Then extend the sequence to the eighth term.**

STEP 1: Find the common ratio.

Create ratios using consecutive terms. Then divide.

$\frac{6}{2} = 6 \div 2 = 3$

$\frac{18}{6} = 18 \div 6 = 3$

$\frac{54}{18} = 54 \div 18 = 3$

STEP 2: Extend the sequence by multiplying by the common ratio.

There are four given terms. The fourth term is 54.

So, $54 \times 3 = 162$, the fifth term

$162 \times 3 = 486$, the sixth term

$486 \times 3 = 1,458$, the seventh term

$1458 \times 3 = 4,374$, the eighth term

SOLUTION: **The common ratio is 3, and the eighth term is 4,374.**

Sample Test Questions

1 Which of the following patterns is a geometric sequence?

A 5, 10, 15, 20,...

B 5, 25, 625, 3,125,...

C 5, 0, 25, 210,...

D 5, 25, 45, 65,...

2 Which of the following patterns is an arithmetic sequence?

A 2, 4, 8, 16,...

B 4, 7, 11, 16,...

C 23, 0, 3, 6,...

D 5, 10, 14, 17,...

3 What is the common difference in this arithmetic sequence?

−5, −2, 1, 4, 7,...

A −3

B 3

C $\frac{2}{5}$

D 7

4 What is the common ratio in this geometric sequence?

5, 20, 80, 320, 1,280,...

A 4

B 15

C 40

D 100

5 What is the ninth term in this sequence?

6, 13, 20, 27, 34,...

A 41

B 55

C 62

D 69

6 What is the sixth term in this sequence?

2, 10, 50, 250,...

Go On ➡

Brief Constructed Response

7 This pattern shows the number of people who joined the fan club of a rock musician in each of the first four weeks.

5, 20, 80, 320,...

Step A   If the pattern continues, how many people will join the fan club in the sixth week?

_____

Step B   Use what you know about number patterns and sequences to explain why your answer is correct. Use words and/or numbers to support your explanation.

_____

_____

_____

_____

Standard 1.A.1.c

Linear and Non-Linear Graphs

You can graph a function by completing a function table, graphing the points, and then connecting the points.

If you can connect the points with a straight line, the function is **linear**. If you cannot connect the points with a straight line, the function is **non-linear**.

Example 1

A function has the rule $y = x - 1$. The graph of four ordered pairs for this function is shown on the coordinate grid below.

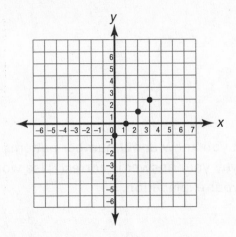

Determine whether the function is linear or non-linear.

STRATEGY: **Connect the points.**

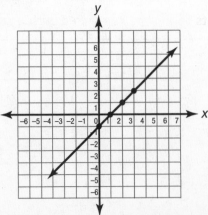

SOLUTION: **Since the points can be connected with a straight line, the function is linear.**

Example 2

A function has the rule $y = x^2 - 3$. The graph of five ordered pairs for the function is shown below.

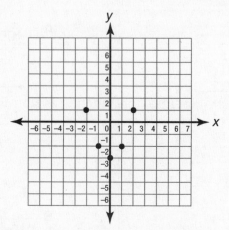

Determine whether the function is linear or non-linear.

STRATEGY: **Connect the points.**

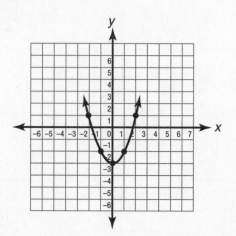

SOLUTION: **Since the points cannot be connected with a straight line, the function is non-linear.**

Sample Test Questions

1 Which graph shows a linear function?

A

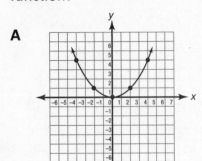

B

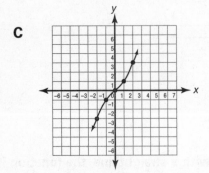

C

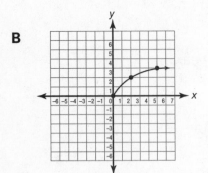

D

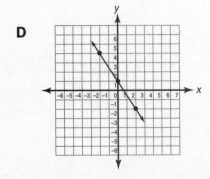

2 Which graph shows a non-linear function?

A

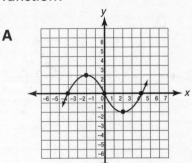

B

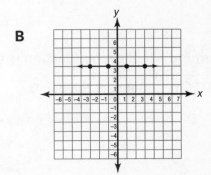

C

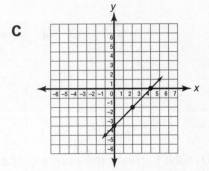

D

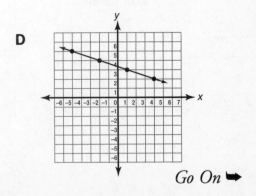

Go On ➡

3 What kind of function does this graph show?

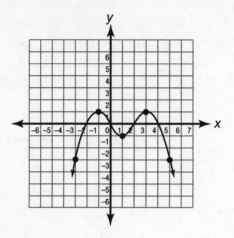

A   linear

B   non-linear

C   both linear and non-linear

D   neither linear nor non-linear

Go On ➡

Brief Constructed Response

4 This is the graph of a function that shows the relationship between Fahrenheit and Celsius temperature.

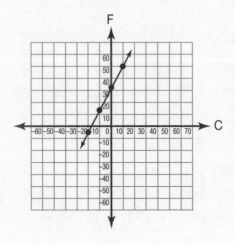

Step A Identify the function as linear or non-linear.

_____

Step B Use what you know about linear and non-linear graphs to explain why your answer is correct. Use words and/or diagrams to support your explanation.

_____

_____

_____

_____

_____

LESSON

3 Order of Operations

For an expression with several operations, in what order do you add, subtract, multiply, and divide?

The answer comes from the following five rules known as the Order of Operations. These rules are applied in the order you see them. This means you apply Rule 1 first, then Rule 2, and so on.

RULES FOR ORDER OF OPERATIONS

1. Do what is inside the parentheses first. If there are brackets within parentheses, do what is inside the brackets first.

2. Simplify all expressions with exponents.

3. Multiply and divide before you add and subtract.

4. Multiply and divide in order from left to right.

5. Add and subtract in order from left to right.

Example 1

$\frac{1}{2} + \frac{1}{2} \times 20$

STRATEGY: Apply Rules 1 to 5 in order.

STEP 1: Use Rule 3. Multiply and divide before you add and subtract.
$\frac{1}{2} \times 20 = 10$

STEP 2: Rule 3 says add after you multiply.
$\frac{1}{2} + 10 = 10\frac{1}{2}$

SOLUTION: The answer is $10\frac{1}{2}$.

Example 2

36 − ([3 × 2²] + 24)

STRATEGY: Apply Rules 1 to 5 in order.

        STEP 1: Use Rule 1. There are brackets within parentheses, so do what is in the brackets first.

$$36 - ([3 \times 2^2] + 24)$$

First simplify the expression with exponents (Rule 2).

$$36 - ([3 \times 4] + 24)$$

Then do what is in the brackets.

$$36 - ([12] + 24)$$

        STEP 2: Use Rule 1 again.

Now do what is inside parentheses.

$$36 - (12 + 24)$$
$$36 - 36$$

        STEP 3: Use Rule 5. Subtract.

$$36 - 36 = 0$$

SOLUTION: The answer is 0.

Example 3

$$\frac{34 + 26}{15} - 3^2$$

STRATEGY: Apply Rules 1 to 5 in order.

        STEP 1: Use Rule 1. An expression in a fraction is treated like an expression in parentheses.

So, first add 34 and 26:

$$\frac{34 + 26}{15} - 3^2$$

$$\frac{60}{15} - 3^2$$

18

STEP 2: Use Rule 2. Simplify the exponent expression.

$$\frac{60}{15} - 3^2$$

$$\frac{60}{15} - 9$$

STEP 3: Use Rule 3. Divide before subtracting.

The fraction bar indicates division.

$$\frac{60}{15} - 9$$

$$4 - 9$$

STEP 4: Use Rule 5. Subtract.

$$4 - 9 = -5$$

SOLUTION: The answer is −5.

Example 3

$$4 + 6\left|-17 + 8\right|$$

STRATEGY: Apply Rules 1 to 5 in order.

STEP 1: Use Rule 1. An expression in absolute value is treated like an expression in parentheses. So, simplify the absolute value first.

$$4 + 6\left|-17 + 8\right|$$

$$4 + 6\left|-9\right|$$

The absolute value is the distance of a number from zero on a number line.

$$\left|-9\right| = 9$$

$$4 + 6\left|-9\right| = 4 + 6(9)$$

STEP 2: Use Rule 3. Multiply before adding.

$$4 + 6(9) = 4 + 54$$

STEP 3: Use Rule 5. Add.

$$4 + 54 = 58$$

SOLUTION: The answer is 58.

Sample Test Questions

Use the Order of Operations Rules to find the answers.

1 $108 \div 12 - 3 + 7 = ?$

    A 19

    B 13

    C 12

    D 10

2 $7 \times 4 \div 2 = ?$

    A 3

    B 7

    C 14

    D 21

3 $6 + 9 \div (6 \div 2) = ?$

    A 9

    B 8

    C 5

    D 3

4 $8 \times 8 \div 8 = ?$

    A 64

    B 48

    C 16

    D 8

5 $10(0.7 - 0.9) = ?$

    A -20

    B -2

    C 2

    D 20

6 $100 \times 7 \div 25 + 10 - 2 = ?$

    A 38

    B 36

    C 18

    D 16

7 $\frac{1}{3} + \frac{1}{3} + (\frac{1}{2} + \frac{1}{6}) = ?$

    A $\frac{1}{8}$

    B $\frac{4}{9}$

    C $\frac{5}{9}$

    D $1\frac{1}{3}$

8 $7 + -5 + -\frac{7}{2} = ?$

    A $-1\frac{1}{2}$

    B $-\frac{1}{2}$

    C $\frac{1}{2}$

    D 1

Go On ➡

9 $\frac{2}{5}(4 + 3\,[21 \div 3]) = ?$

A $\frac{28}{5}$

B 10

C 15

D $\frac{98}{5}$

10 $30 \div 5 \times (2 + 8) \div 2 + 5 = ?$

A $\frac{60}{7}$

B 12.5

C 35

D 67

11 $5 \times (4 - 2) \times 6 \div 3 = ?$

A 60

B 40

C 20

D 10

12 $4 \times |-3 \times 5| - 60 = ?$

A −60

B −52

C 0

D 68

13 $2 \times 62 - 100 = ?$

A 72

B 36

C 24

D 18

Go On ➡

Brief Constructed Response

14 Daryl created this expression using the numbers 2, 3, 4, 5, and 6.

$$4 + 6(2 - 5) \div 3$$

Step A Find the value of Daryl's expression.

_____

Step B Use what you know about the Order of Operations to explain why your answer is correct. Use words and/or numbers to support your explanation.

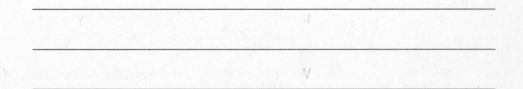

_____

_____

_____

_____

_____

STOP

LESSON 4

Writing and Evaluating Expressions

Letters that stand for numbers are called **variables.** You can use variables to translate word expressions to mathematical expressions.

A mathematical **expression** is any group of numbers and variables. Here are some examples:

$$6x \qquad 2(a - 9) \qquad (8n + 12) \div 4 \qquad w \div 4 + w - 8$$

Example 1

Write a mathematical expression for this word expression:

three times a number, increased by 5

STRATEGY: **Choose a variable and look for key words that stand for mathematical operations.**

STEP 1:   Choose a variable.

Let n = the number

STEP 2:   Use the key words for mathematical operations.

times means *multiply*

increased by means *add*

three times a number increased by 5

$\quad$ 3 $\quad \times \quad$ n $\quad\quad$ + $\quad\quad$ 5

When a number is multiplied by a variable, leave out the multiplication symbol.

So, $3 \times n$ can be written as $3n$.

SOLUTION: **A mathematical expression for three times a number, increased by 5 is $3n + 5$.**

If you know the value of a variable in an expression, you can substitute the value in the expression to **evaluate** the expression.

Example 2

Evaluate $4(m + 7) - 5$ when $m = 0.5$.

STRATEGY: **Substitute 0.5 for m and use the order of operations.**

STEP 1: Substitute 0.5 for m.

$$4(m + 7) - 5$$
$$4(0.5 + 7) - 5$$

STEP 2: Use the order of operations.

$$4(0.5 + 7) - 5 = 4(7.5) - 5$$
$$= 30 - 5$$
$$= 25$$

SOLUTION: **The result is 25.**

An expression may have more than one kind of variable.

Example 3

Evaluate $3x + 2y$ when $x = 2$ and $y = -\frac{1}{2}$.

STRATEGY: **Substitute the values for the variables and use the order of operations.**

STEP 1: Substitute 2 for x and $-\frac{1}{2}$ for y.

$$3x + 2y$$
$$3(2) + 2\left(-\frac{1}{2}\right)$$

STEP 2: Use the order of operations.

$$3(2) + 2\left(-\frac{1}{2}\right) = 6 + -1$$
$$= 5$$

SOLUTION: **The result is 5.**

Sample Test Questions

In Questions 1–4, find the mathematical expression that matches the word expression.

1 100 decreased by the quotient of a number and 8

- **A** $100 - (8 \div n)$
- **B** $100 - (n \div 8)$
- **C** $(n \div 8) - 100$
- **D** $(n \div 8) + 100$

2 The product of a number and 85, divided by 17

- **A** $(n + 85) \div 17$
- **B** $1 - 7 \div (85n)$
- **C** $85n \times 17$
- **D** $85n \div 17$

3 The sum of a number and 80, multiplied by the difference of the number and 50

- **A** $(n + 80) \times (n + 50)$
- **B** $(n - 80) \times (n - 50)$
- **C** $(n - 80) \times (n + 50)$
- **D** $(n + 80) \times (n - 50)$

4 150 less than half a number, divided by –5

- **A** $(150 - \frac{1}{2}x) \div -5$
- **B** $(\frac{1}{2}x - 150) \div -5$
- **C** $-5 \div (150 - \frac{1}{2}x)$
- **D** $-5 \div (\frac{1}{2}x - 150)$

5 What does this expression mean?

$$7y - 7x$$

- **A** Multiply 7, y, and x.
- **B** Multiply 7 and y and then subtract the result of multiplying 7 and x.
- **C** Subtract the product of 7 and y from the product of 7 and x.
- **D** Add the product of 7 and x to the product of 7 and y.

6 Evaluate $16x$ when $x = \frac{1}{4}$.

- **A** $\frac{1}{4}$
- **C** 8
- **B** 4
- **D** 64

7 Evaluate $48 - 6n$ when $n = 8$.

- **A** 0
- **C** 96
- **B** 34
- **D** 336

8 Evaluate $x + 17$ when $x = -25.5$.

- **A** −42.5
- **C** 8.5
- **B** −8.5
- **D** 42.5

9 Evaluate $12m - 9n$ when $m = 5$ and $n = 4$.

Go On ➡

25

Brief Constructed Response

10   Tanya bought notebooks costing $6 each and pens costing $4 each. Both prices included tax. Letting *n* stand for the number of notebooks and *p* stand for the number pens, the expression for the total amount she spent is given by the expression $6n + 4p$.

     Step A   If Tanya bought 5 notebooks and 3 pens, how much did she spend in all?

_____

     Step B   Use what you know about writing and evaluating expressions to explain why your answer is correct. Use words and/or numbers to support your explanation.

_____

_____

_____

_____

Standard 1.B.1.d

Combining Like Terms of Expressions

Some expressions contain like terms. Like terms have the same variables raised to the same power. Here are some examples:

$5x$ and $-3x$ $4ab$ and $10ab$ $2x^2$ and $\frac{1}{2}x^2$ $1def$ and $9def$

Example 1

Simplify this expression by combining like terms.

$9a + 15a$

STRATEGY: **Use the distributive property.**

STEP 1:   Use the distributive property to write the sum as a product.

$9a + 15a = a(9 + 15)$

STEP 2:   Do the operation in parentheses.

$a(9 + 15) = a \times 24$

STEP 3:   Use the commutative property.

$a \times 24 = 24 \times a = 24a$

SOLUTION: $9a + 15a = 24a$

Example 2

Simplify this expression by combining like terms.

$$25x^2 - 10x^2 + 5x - 25$$

STRATEGY: **Use the distributive property.**

The only like terms are $25x^2$ and $-10x^2$. The term $5x$ has a different exponent (1), so $5x$ cannot be combined with $25x^2$ and $-10x^2$.

Use the distributive property to write $25x^2 - 10x^2$ as a product.

$$25x^2 - 10x^2 + 5x - 25 = x^2(25 - 10) + 5x - 25$$
$$= 15x^2 + 5x - 25$$

SOLUTION: $25x^2 - 10x^2 + 5x - 25 = 15x^2 + 5x - 25$

Example 3

Simplify this expression by combining like terms.

$$\frac{1}{4}xyz + 8 + \frac{3}{4}xyz - 5$$

STRATEGY: **Use the commutative property and then the distributive property.**

STEP 1: Use the commutative property of addition to rearrange the terms.

$$\frac{1}{4}xyz + 8 + \frac{3}{4}xyz - 5 = \frac{1}{4}xyz + \frac{3}{4}xyz + 8 - 5$$

STEP 2: Combine the terms with variables.

$$\frac{1}{4}xyz + \frac{3}{4}xyz + 8 - 5$$

$$xyz(\frac{1}{4} + \frac{3}{4}) + 8 - 5$$

$$xyz(1) + 8 - 5$$

$$1xyz + 8 - 5$$

$1xyz$ is the same as $1 \times xyz$, or xyz, so $1xyz + 8 - 5 = xyz + 8 - 5$.

STEP 3: Combine the terms with no variables.

$$xyz + 8 - 5 = xyz + 3$$

SOLUTION: $\frac{1}{4}xyz + 8 + \frac{3}{4}xyz - 5 = xyz + 3$

Sample Test Questions

Simplify the expressions in Questions 1–6 by combining like terms.

1 $8m + 16m$

  A $8m$

  B $24m$

  C $24m^2$

  D $32m$

2 $n + n - 18$

  A $n^2 - 18$

  B -18

  C $2n - 18$

  D $n - 18$

3 $16rst - 24rst$

  A $-8rst$

  B $8rst$

  C $8r^2s^2t^2$

  D $40rst$

4 $15df + 27df - 9df$

  A $33d^3f^3$

  B $33df$

  C $51d^2f^2$

  D $51df$

5 $\frac{1}{5}x + 6 + \frac{3}{5}x$

  A $\frac{4}{5}x + 6$

  B $(6\frac{4}{5})x$

  C $x + 6$

  D $\frac{4}{5}x^2 + 6$

6 $a^2 + 3a^2 + a$

  A $5a^2$

  B $4a^2 + a$

  C $4a^4 + a$

  D $3a^2 + 2a$

Go On ➡

Brief Constructed Response

7   This expression represents the area of a rectangle:

$$n^2 + 3n + 6n + 18$$

Step A   Simplify the expression by combining like terms.

_____

Step B   Use what you know about combining like terms to explain why your answer is correct. Use words and/or numbers to support your explanation.

_____

_____

_____

_____

_____

Standard 1.B.2.a, b

LESSON 6

Using and Solving Equations

In algebra you frequently have to translate word sentences into mathematical sentences. A sentence using = is called an equation.

Example 1

After 8 students were transferred out of an eighth-grade class, there were 19 students remaining. Write an equation to find the number of students in the class before the students were transferred.

STRATEGY: **Use a variable and translate the words into an equation.**

> **STEP 1:** Let *n* stand for the number of students in the class before the transfer.
>
> **STEP 2:** Write the equation.

number of students before the transfer − 8 = number of students after the transfer

$$n \qquad\qquad -8 = \qquad\qquad 19$$

SOLUTION: **An equation to find the number of students in the class before the students were transferred is *n* − 8 = 19.**

Example 2

Sarah wants to buy a calculator that costs $54, including tax. She already has $36 saved. She can save $9 per week. Write an equation to find the number of weeks she needs to save.

STRATEGY: **Use a variable and translate the words into an equation.**

> **STEP 1:** Let *n* stand for the number of weeks Sarah needs to save.
>
> **STEP 2:** Write an expression for the amount she can save in *n* weeks.
>
> If she saves $9 in one week, she can save $9 \times n$, or $9n$, in *n* weeks.

STEP 3: Write the equation.

Amount of money saved in n weeks + amount of money already saved = $54			
$9n$	+	36	= 54

SOLUTION: **An equation that can be used to find the number of weeks Sarah needs to save is $9n + 36 = 54$.**

"Solving" an equation means finding the number represented by the variable. To solve an equation, isolate the variable. This means get the variable by itself on one side of the equation.

Solving Equations by Adding or Subtracting

Example 3

Solve the equation $-2.8 + n = 4.3$

STRATEGY: **Isolate the variable.**

    STEP 1: Start with the equation: $-2.8 + n = 4.3$

    STEP 2: Get rid of the -2.8 on the left side of the equation.

                  Add 2.8 to both sides of the equation:

$$(-2.8 + \mathbf{2.8}) + n = 4.3 + \mathbf{2.8}$$

    STEP 3: Do the math.

$$(-2.8 + \mathbf{2.8}) + n = 4.3 + \mathbf{2.8}$$
$$0 + n = 7.1$$
$$n = 7.1$$

SOLUTION: **The solution is 7.1.**

Example 4

Solve the equation $x + \frac{1}{10} = \frac{4}{5}$

STRATEGY: **Isolate the variable.**

Subtract $\frac{1}{10}$ from both sides of the equation.

$$x + \frac{1}{10} = \frac{4}{5}$$

$$x + \left(\frac{1}{10} - \frac{1}{10}\right) = \frac{4}{5} - \frac{1}{10}$$

$$x + 0 = \frac{4}{5} - \frac{1}{10}$$

$$x = \frac{4}{5} - \frac{1}{10} = \frac{8}{10} - \frac{1}{10} = \frac{7}{10}$$

SOLUTION: The solution is $\frac{7}{10}$.

Solving Equations by Multiplying

Example 5

Solve the equation $18n = 72$

STRATEGY: **Isolate the variable.**

STEP 1:   Start with the equation: $18n = 72$

STEP 2:   Get rid of the 18 that multiplies n.

Use the reciprocal of 18 which is $\frac{1}{18}$.

$$\frac{1}{18}(18n) = \frac{1}{18}(72)$$

STEP 3:   Do the math.

$$\frac{1}{18}(18n) = \frac{1}{18}(72)$$

$$\left(\frac{1}{18} \times 18\right)n = \frac{1}{18} \times 72$$

$$1n = 4$$

$$n = 4$$

SOLUTION: **The solution is 4.**

Example 6

Solve the equation $\frac{k}{3} = -17$

STRATEGY: Isolate the variable.

STEP 1: Start with the equation: $\frac{k}{3} = -17$

STEP 2: Get rid of the 3 that divides k.

Multiply both sides by 3:

$$3\left(\frac{k}{3}\right) = 3(-17)$$
$$k = -51$$

SOLUTION: The solution is −51.

Solving Equations Using More Than One Operation

Example 7

Solve the equation $2a + 6a + a = 54$

STRATEGY: Isolate the variable.

STEP 1: First combine like terms.
$$2a + 6a + a = 54$$
$$(2 + 6 + 1)a = 54$$
$$9a = 54$$

STEP 2: Multiply both sides by $\frac{1}{9}$.
$$\frac{1}{9}(9a) = \frac{1}{9}(54)$$

STEP 3: Do the math.
$$\frac{1}{9}(9a) = \frac{1}{9}(54)$$
$$\left(\frac{1}{9} \times 9\right)a = \frac{1}{9} \times 54$$
$$1a = 6$$
$$a = 6$$

SOLUTION: The solution is 6.

Example 8

Solve the equation from Example 2 of this lesson:

$$9n + 36 = 54$$

STRATEGY: Isolate *n*.

STEP 1: Subtract 36 from both sides.

$$9n + 36 - 36 = 54 - 36$$

STEP 2: Do the math.

$$9n + 36 - 36 = 54 - 36$$
$$9n + 0 = 18$$
$$9n = 18$$

STEP 3: Multiply both sides by $\frac{1}{9}$.

$$\frac{1}{9}(9n) = \frac{1}{9}(18)$$

STEP 4: Do the math.

$$\frac{1}{9}(9n) = \frac{1}{9}(18)$$
$$n = 2$$

SOLUTION: **The solution is 2. In Example 2, that means that Sarah will have to save for 2 weeks to buy the calculator.**

Sample Test Questions

1 After Vernon made a deposit of $136, the new balance in his savings account was $540. Which equation can be used to find b, the balance in his account before he made the deposit?

A $b - 136 = 540$

B $b + 136 = 540$

C $136b = 540$

D $\dfrac{b}{136} = 540$

2 Two friends went out to dinner and ordered exactly the same items from the menu. Their combined tip came to $7.40. Their total cost including tip was $56.20. Which equation can be used to find d, the amount each friend paid for dinner without the tip?

A $d + \$7.40 = \$56.20$

B $d - \$7.40 = \$56.20$

C $2d + \$7.40 = \$56.20$

D $2d - \$7.40 = \$56.20$

3 In the year 2000, the population of Gene's town was 942. This was 3 times the population of the town in 1980. Which equation can be used to find p, the population of the town in 1980?

A $942 - p = 3$

B $3p = 942$

C $\dfrac{p}{3} = 942$

D $942 - p = 1980$

4 The sum of two consecutive numbers, x and $(x + 1)$, is 397. Which equation can be used to find x, the first of the two numbers?

A $x + (x + 1) = 397$

B $x - (x + 1) = 397$

C $x(x + 1) = 397$

D $x + x = 397$

Go On ➡

In Questions 5–12, solve the equation.

5 $-15 + c = 75$

A −90
B −60
C 60
D 90

6 $d - 2.7 = -2.0$

A −4.7
B −0.7
C 0.7
D 4.7

7 $13n = 91$

A 7
B 8
C 9
D 78

8 $4b + 9b - 2b = 132$

A 11
B 12
C 13
D 22

9 $\frac{t}{18} = -6$

A −3
B −24
C −54
D −108

10 $5n - 50 = 120$

A −34
B −14
C 14
D 34

11 $6x - 4x + 57 = 87$

A −72
B −15
C 15
D 72

12 $5x + x = \frac{6}{25}$

A $\frac{1}{125}$
B $\frac{1}{25}$
C $\frac{6}{125}$
D $\frac{6}{25}$

Go On ➡

Brief Constructed Response

13 A cab ride cost $33. This equation can be used to find the number of miles *m* of the trip.

$$33 = 5m - 2$$

Step A How many miles was the trip?

_____

Step B Use what you know about solving equations to explain why your answer is correct. Use words and/or numbers to support your explanation.

_____

_____

_____

_____

LESSON 7

Solving Inequalities and Graphing Solutions

Some mathematical sentences are inequalities.

Example 1

Write a mathematical sentence for this:

The sum of a number and 47 is greater than 55.

STRATEGY: **Translate each phrase into symbols.**

STEP 1: Translate "The sum of a number and 47."

Let x stand for the number.

$x + 47$

STEP 2: Translate "is greater than 55."

> 55

STEP 3: Translate the entire sentence into symbols.

The sum of a number and 47 is greater than 55.

$x + 47 > 55$

SOLUTION: **"The sum of a number and 47 is greater than 55" becomes $x + 47 > 55$.**

Example 2

Write a mathematical sentence for this:

Twenty-four more than half a number is less than 80.

STRATEGY: **Translate each phrase into symbols.**

STEP 1: Translate "half a number."

Use n for the number, so "half a number" is $\frac{1}{2}n$.

STEP 2: Translate "Twenty-four more than half a number."

$\frac{1}{2}n + 24$

STEP 3: Translate "is less than 80."

< 80

STEP 4: Translate "Twenty-four more than half a number is less than 80."

$\frac{1}{2}n + 24 < 80$

SOLUTION: "Twenty-four more than half a number is less than 80" becomes $\frac{1}{2}n + 24 < 80$.

Solving an inequality is similar to solving an equation.

Example 3

Solve the inequality: $n + 3n - 12 > 8$

STRATEGY: Solve the inequality as you would an equation.

STEP 1: Combine like terms.

$n + 3n - 12 > 8$

$1n + 3n - 12 > 8$

$4n - 12 > 8$

STEP 2: Do the step-by-step math.

$4n - 12 > 8$

$4n - 12 + 12 > 8 + 12$

$4n + 0 > 20$

$4n > 20$

$n > 5$

SOLUTION: The solution of the inequality $n + 3n - 12 > 8$ is $n > 5$.

You can use a number line to graph an inequality.

Example 4

Graph the solution of the inequality $2n > -8$.

STRATEGY: **Solve the inequality and graph the solution on a number line.**

STEP 1: Solve the inequality.

$$2n > -8$$

$$\frac{1}{2}(2n) > \frac{1}{2}(-8)$$

$$n > -4$$

STEP 2: Draw a number line.

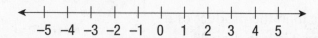

STEP 3: Read $n > -4$ as "n is greater than -4."

SOLUTION: **Draw the graph of "n is greater than -4" on the number line:**

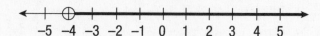

NOTES: Notice the following things about the graph in Example 4:

- The graph starts at -4 and extends to the right to include ALL numbers greater than -4.

- There is an open circle at -4. This shows that -4 itself is NOT included in the inequality $n > -4$.

- If the inequality had been $n \geq -4$ ("n is greater than or equal to -4"), then the dot would be filled in, like this:

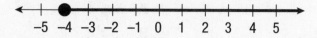

Sample Test Questions

Represent each statement in Questions 1–3 with an inequality.

1 The quotient of a number and 14 is greater than 70.

    A $n \div 14 < 70$

    B $n \div 14 \geq 70$

    C $n \div 14 > 70$

    D $n \div 14 \leq 70$

2 Fifteen less than the product of a number and 3 is less than 45.

    A $3n - 15 < 45$

    B $15 - 3n < 45$

    C $3n - 15 \leq 45$

    D $15 + 3n < 45$

3 Twice the difference of a number and 26 is greater than 52.

    A $2x - 26 > 52$

    B $26 - 2x > 52$

    C $2(x - 26) \geq 52$

    D $2(x - 26) > 52$

For Questions 4–7, find the solution of each inequality.

4 $7x + 3 > 24$

    A $x > 3$

    B $x < 3$

    C $x > 4$

    D $x < 4$

5 $6n - 19 \leq -25$

    A $n \leq -1$

    B $n \geq 1$

    C $n \geq -1$

    D $n \geq 1$

6 $2x + 3x - 5 < 30$

    A $x < 5$

    B $x < 7$

    C $x > 5$

    D $x > 7$

7 $4n + 9n - 5n \geq 72$

    A $n \geq 4$

    B $n \geq 8$

    C $n > 9$

    D $n \geq 9$

Go On ➡

8 Which inequality is graphed below?

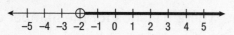

A $x < -2$

B $x \leq -2$

C $x > -2$

D $x \geq -2$

9 Which inequality is graphed below?

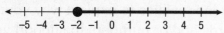

A $x \leq -2$

B $x > -2$

C $x < -2$

D $x \leq -2$

10 Which graph is the solution of this inequality?

$$4n - 1 < 15$$

A

B

C

D

Go On ➡

Extended Constructed Response

11 This inequality represents Tara's budget, where *n* stands for the number of weeks she'll have to save in order to have at least $14.

$$2n + 4 \geq 14$$

Step A Find the solution of the inequality.

_____

Step B • Use what you know about inequalities to explain why your answer is correct. Use words and/or numbers to support your explanation.

_____

_____

_____

• On the number line below graph the solution of your inequality. Use what you know about graphing inequalities to explain why your graph is correct.

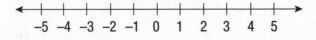

_____

_____

_____

LESSON 8
Identifying Equivalent Equations

Equations that have the same solution are equivalent equations.

Example

Which equation is equivalent to $3x + 2 = 8$?

A $x + 4x = 5$ **B** $x + 2 = 6$ **C** $6x + 5 = 11$ **D** $4x - 3 = 5$

STRATEGY: Solve the given equation and each of the equation choices and compare the solutions.

    STEP 1: Solve the given equation.

$3x + 2 = 8$	Subtract 2 from both sides.
$3x = 6$	Multiply both sides by $\frac{1}{3}$.
$x = 2$	An equivalent equation must have a solution of 2.

    STEP 2: Solve Choice A.

$x + 4x = 5$	Combine like terms.
$5x = 5$	Multiply both sides by $\frac{1}{5}$.
$x = 1$	⇐ not equivalent to the given equation

    STEP 3: Solve Choice B.

$x + 2 = 6$	Subtract 2 from both sides.
$x = 4$	⇐ not equivalent to the given equation

    STEP 4: Solve Choice C.

$6x + 5 = 11$	Subtract 5 from both sides.
$6x = 6$	Multiply both sides by $\frac{1}{6}$.
$x = 1$	⇐ not equivalent to the given equation

    STEP 5: Solve Choice D.

$4x - 3 = 5$	Add 3 to both sides.
$4x = 8$	Multiply both sides by $\frac{1}{4}$.
$x = 2$	⇐ equivalent to the given equation

SOLUTION: The equation that is equivalent to $3x + 2 = 8$ is $4x - 3 = 5$, Choice D.

When you solve an equation step by step, the equation at each step is equivalent to the original equation. For example, in Step 1 of the Example above, all these equations are equivalent:

$$3x + 2 = 8 \qquad 3x = 6 \qquad x = 2$$

45

Sample Test Questions

1 Which equation is equivalent to $3x + 1 = 46$?

- **A** $5x = 20$
- **B** $2x - 16 = 14$
- **C** $5x + 10 = 20$
- **D** $x - 7 = 9$

2 Which equation is equivalent to $7x - 4 = 17$?

- **A** $7x = 13$
- **B** $7x = -13$
- **C** $7x = 21$
- **D** $7x = -21$

3 Which equation is not equivalent to $4x + 5x + 8 = 71$?

- **A** $9x = 63$
- **B** $9x = 79$
- **C** $9x + 8 = 71$
- **D** $x = 7$

4 Which equation is not equivalent to $x = 9$?

- **A** $2x + 5 = 23$
- **B** $\frac{x}{3} + 5 = 8$
- **C** $4x - 30 = 6$
- **D** $3x + 1 = 26$

Go On ➡

Brief Constructed Response

5 This equation shows the solution of an equation:

$n = 5$

Step A Find an equation that is equivalent to $n = 5$.

_____

Step B Use what you know about equivalent equations to explain why your answer is correct. Use words and/or numbers to support your explanation.

_____

_____

_____

_____

LESSON
9 Applying Formulas

Mathematics and science are full of formulas. You need to know how to substitute into formulas to find answers in order to solve problems.

Example

The formula for simple interest is:

$i = prt$

i stands for the amount of interest.

p stands for the principal (the amount invested).

r stands for the rate of interest.

t stands for the length of time the principal is invested.

What is the amount of simple interest for an investment of $300 invested for 3 years at a rate of 6%?

STRATEGY: **Substitute the values in the formula and simplify.**

STEP 1: Change the interest rate to a decimal.
6% = 0.06

STEP 2: Substitute the values in the formula $i = prt$
$i = ?$ $p = 300$ $r = 0.06$ $t = 3$
$i = prt = (300)(0.06)(3)$

STEP 3: Do the math.
$i = prt = (300)(0.06)(3) = 54$

SOLUTION: **The amount of interest after 3 years is $54.**

Sample Test Questions

1 Suppose you invest $400 in a government bond that guarantees 8% simple interest per year. How much would your investment be worth after 1 year? (Use the formula $i = prt$.)

A $32   C $432

B $320   D $464

2 The formula for the area of a trapezoid is $A = \frac{1}{2} h(b_1 + b_2)$. In this formula, A stands for the area, h stands for the height of the trapezoid, b_1 stands for the length of one of the two bases of the trapezoid, and b_2 stands for the length of the other base. Find the area of a trapezoid with height equal to 10 cm and the two bases equal to 15 cm and 20 cm.

A 175 cm^2 C 190 cm^2

B 180 cm^2 D 250 cm^2

3 The formula for the volume of a rectangular prism is $V = lwh$. In this formula, V stands for the volume of the prism, l stands for the length, w stands for the width, and h stands for the height. What is the volume of a rectangular prism with a length of 9 inches, a width of 7 inches, and a height of 6 inches?

A 22 in.^{3} C 378 in.^{3}

B 318 in.^{3} D 398 in.^{3}

4 The formula for finding the total price of an item, including tax, is $T = p(1 + r)$. In this formula, T stands for the total price including tax, p stands for the price before tax, and r stands for the rate of tax. What is the total price of a CD when $p = \$12.50$ and $r = 6\%$?

A $7.50

B $13.25

C $18.50

D $20.00

5 The formula for converting temperature in degrees Fahrenheit to degrees Celsius is $F = \frac{9}{5}C + 32$. What is the temperature in Fahrenheit degrees when the temperature in degrees Celsius is $-20°$?

A $-36°$

B $-4°$

C $13.6°$

D $68°$

Go On ➡

Brief Constructed Response

6 $350 is invested at 7% simple interest for 2 years.

     Step A   How much interest does the investment earn after 2 years?

_____

     Step B   Use what you know about formulas to explain why your answer is correct. Use words and/or numbers to support your explanation.

_____

_____

_____

_____

STOP

Standard 1.C.1.a

Drawing Graphs of Linear Equations

An equation such as $y = -2x + 3$ has solutions that are ordered pairs (x,y) where the x-values are the input values and the y-values are the corresponding output values. The equation $y = -2x + 3$ is a linear equation because the graphs of the ordered-pair solutions form a straight line.

Example

Graph the equation $y = -2x + 3$.

STRATEGY: **Graph several ordered pairs and connect them with a straight line.**

STEP 1: Make a table of x-values and y-values. Use the table to find three or four ordered pairs.

X	$y = -2x + 3$	y	(x,y)
−1	$y = -2(-1) + 3 = 2 + 3 = 5$	5	(−1,5)
0	$y = -2(0) + 3 = 0 + 3 = 3$	3	(0,3)
1	$y = -2(1) + 3 = -2 + 3 = 1$	1	(1,1)
2	$y = -2(2) + 3 = -4 + 3 = -1$	−1	(2,−1)

STEP 2: Graph the ordered pairs and draw a straight line through the points.

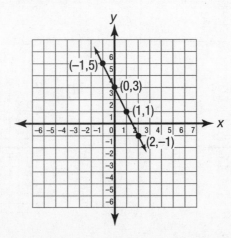

SOLUTION: **The graph in Step 2 is the graph of $y = -2x + 3$.**

51

Sample Test Questions

1 Which is the graph of the linear equation $y = x - 4$?

A

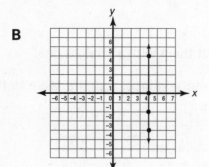

B

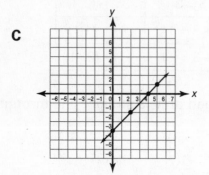

C

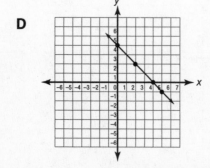

D

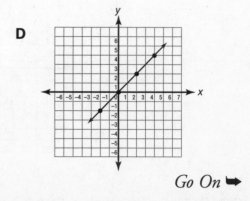

2 Which is the graph of the linear equation $y = 2x - 5$?

A

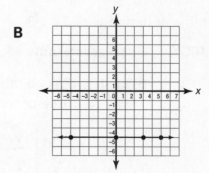

B

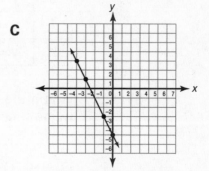

C

D

Go On ➡

3 Which linear equation has this graph?

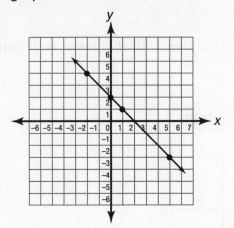

A $y = x + 2$

B $y = 2x + 2$

C $y = -x + 2$

D $y = -x - 2$

4 Which linear equation has this graph?

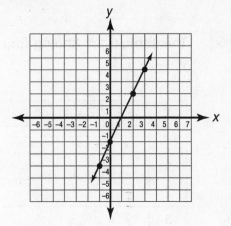

A $y = 2x$

B $y = 2x - 2$

C $y = -2x - 2$

D $y = 2x + 2$

Go On ➡

Extended Constructed Response

5 This table is for finding four ordered pair solutions for the linear equation $y = -2x + 4$.

X	$y = -2x + 4$	y	(x,y)
−1			
1			
2			
3			

Step A Complete the table to find the four ordered pairs.

Go On ➡

Step B • Use what you know about finding solutions of linear equations to explain why your answer is correct. Use words and/or numbers to support your explanation.

_____

_____

_____

_____

• Use the values from the table to graph $y = -2x + 4$ on the coordinate grid below. Use your graph to explain why $y = -2x + 4$ is linear.

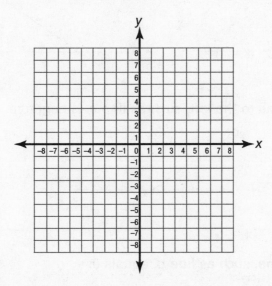

STOP

LESSON

11 Introduction to Slope

The slope of a line refers to the degree to which a line slants with respect to a horizontal line. Imagine the slope of a hill.

Positive, Negative, and Zero Slopes

The slope of a line is a number. It can be positive, negative, or 0.

The slopes of lines that lean to the right, like lines *a* and *b*, are positive.

Since line *a* is steeper than line *b*, the slope of line *a* is greater than the slope of line *b*.

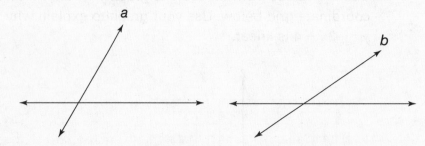

The slope of a line that leans to the left, such as line *c*, is negative.

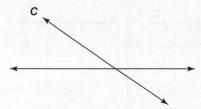

The slope of a horizontal line, such as line *d*, equals 0.

A vertical line leans neither to the right nor to the left. Therefore, a vertical line such as line *e* below has no slope, or an undefined slope.

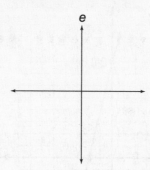

Remember that a *slope of 0* (a horizontal line) is NOT the same as *no slope* (a vertical line).

Example 1

Are the slopes of lines *x*, *y*, and *z* positive, negative, or 0?

STRATEGY: **Check each line to see if it leans to the right, to the left, or if it is horizontal.**

Line *x* leans to the left.

Line *y* is horizontal.

Line *z* leans to the right.

SOLUTION: **The slope of line *x* is negative. The slope of line *y* is 0. The slope of line *z* is positive.**

Finding the Slope

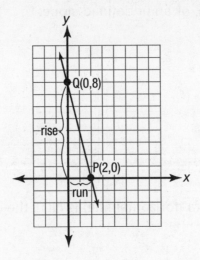

Follow these six steps to find the slope.

1. Note the two points where the line crosses the *x*-axis and the *y*-axis. These are P and Q in the diagram above.

    P = (2,0) and Q = (0,8)

2. Find the distance from Q to the origin (0,0)—it is 8 units. This number is called the **rise**.

3. Find the distance from P to the origin (0,0)—it is 2 units. This number is called the **run**.

4. Form this fraction:

    $\dfrac{\text{rise}}{\text{run}} = \dfrac{8}{2}$

5. Check to see if the slope is positive, or negative, or 0. In this case, the line leans to the left, so the slope is negative.

6. Since the slope is negative, change the fraction to negative:
    The slope is $-\dfrac{\text{rise}}{\text{run}} = -\dfrac{8}{2}$, or $-\dfrac{4}{1}$.

Example 2

Find the slope of this line.

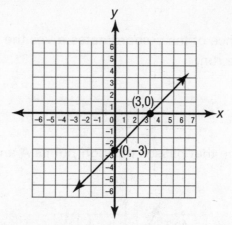

STRATEGY: **Follow the steps from the previous page.**

STEP 1: Find the rise.

The rise is the distance from (0,–3) to the origin.

The rise is 3.

STEP 2: Find the run.

The run is the distance from (3,0) to the origin.

The run is 3.

STEP 3: Form the fraction: $\dfrac{\text{rise}}{\text{run}} = \dfrac{3}{3} = \dfrac{1}{1}$

STEP 4: Is the slope of this line positive, or negative, or 0?

The line leans to the right, so the slope is positive.

SOLUTION: **The slope is $\dfrac{1}{1}$ or 1.**

If you know the coordinates of any two points on a line, such as (x_1, y_1) and (x_2, y_2), you can find the slope of the line using this formula:

$$\frac{y_1 - y_2}{x_1 - x_2}$$

In this formula, the difference of the y-coordinates gives the rise and the difference of the x-coordinates gives the run.

Example 3

What is the slope of the line that passes through points A and B?

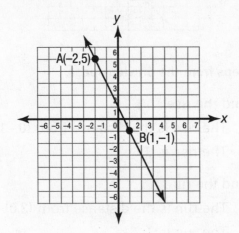

STRATEGY: **Use the slope formula.**

STEP 1:   Choose values for (x_1, y_1) and (x_2, y_2).

Let $A(-2, 5) = (x_1, y_1)$, so $x_1 = -2$ and $y_1 = 5$.

Let $B(1, -1) = (x_2, y_2)$, so $x_2 = 1$ and $y_2 = -1$.

STEP 2:   Substitute in the formula.

$$\frac{y_1 - y_2}{x_1 - x_2} = \frac{5 - (-1)}{-2 - 1}$$

STEP 3:   Do the math.

$$\frac{5 - (-1)}{-2 - 1} = \frac{6}{-3} = \frac{-2}{1}$$

SOLUTION: **The slope of the line is $\frac{-2}{1}$, or -2.**

Many of the linear equations you have studied are in this form:

$$y = mx + b$$

In this form, the letter m is the coefficient of x. That means that m is a number that is multiplied by variable x. The letter b stands for a constant. A constant is a number in a formula that does not change.

For example, in a linear equation such as $y = 2x + 1$, the coefficient of x is 2 and the constant is 1.

If a linear equation is in the form $y = mx + b$, then m is the value of the slope.

Example 4

What is the slope of the graph of the linear equation $y = -x + 3$?

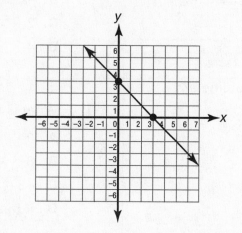

STRATEGY: The equation is in the form $y = mx + b$. Identify the coefficient of x.

Since $-x = -1x$, $y = -x + 3$ is the same as $y = -1x + 3$.
The coefficient of x is -1.

SOLUTION: The slope is -1, meaning that you can think of the slope as $-\frac{1}{1}$.
You can check the answer by looking at the graph to see
where the line intersects the x-axis and y-axis.

Sample Test Questions

Use this diagram for Questions 1–4.

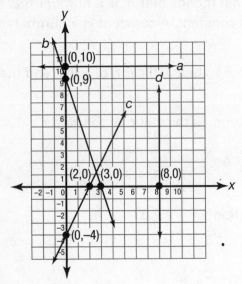

1 What is the slope of line *a*?

A   0

B   1

C   10

D   It has no slope.

2 What is the slope of line *b*?

A   9

B   3

C   −3

D $\frac{1}{3}$

3 What is the slope of line *c*?

A   −4

B   −2

C   2

D   4

4 What is the slope of line *d*?

A   0

B   8

C   −8

D   It has no slope.

Go On ➡

Use this diagram for Questions 5 and 6.

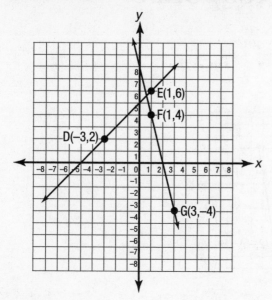

5 What is the slope of the line that passes through points D and E?

A $\frac{-2}{1}$

B $\frac{-1}{1}$

C $\frac{1}{1}$

D $\frac{2}{1}$

6 What is the slope of the line that passes through points F and G?

A $\frac{-4}{1}$

B $\frac{-2}{1}$

C $\frac{2}{1}$

D $\frac{4}{1}$

7 What is the slope of the line with equation $y = 8x + 15$?

A $-\frac{8}{1}$

B $\frac{1}{8}$

C $\frac{8}{1}$

D $\frac{15}{1}$

8 What is the slope of the line with equation $y = -4x - 1$?

A $-\frac{4}{1}$

B $-\frac{1}{4}$

C $\frac{4}{1}$

D $-\frac{1}{1}$

Go On ➡

Brief Constructed Response

9   This is the graph of a linear equation.

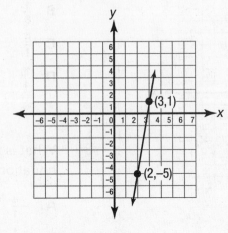

Step A   What is the slope of the line?

_____

Step B   Use what you know about finding slope to explain why your answer is correct. Use words and/or numbers to support your explanation.

_____

_____

_____

_____

_____

Progress Check for Lessons 1–11

1 What is the ninth term in this sequence?

8, 15, 22, 29, 36,…

A 43

B 57

C 64

D 71

2 What is the seventh term in this sequence?

2, 8, 32, 128,…

A 256

B 512

C 2,048

D 8,192

3 What kind of function does this graph show?

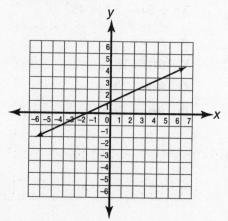

A linear

B non-linear

C both linear and non-linear

D neither linear nor non-linear

4 What is an expression for *fifty-eight decreased by the product of a number and seven?*

A $7n - 58$

B $58 - n \div 7$

C $58 - (n + 7)$

D $58 - 7n$

5 Evaluate $2x + 39$ when $x = -4.5$.

A –30

B –9

C 9

D 30

6 $7 + 5(12 - [8 \div 4]) = ?$

A 47

B 57

C 67

D 77

7 Simplify this expression by combining like terms.

$$n^2 + 4n + 3n + 12$$

A $n^2 + 7n + 12$

B $8n^2 + 12$

C $8n^4 + 12$

D $n^2 + 12n + 12$

Go On ➡

8 Jessica wants to buy a CD player that costs $96, including tax. She already has $64 saved. She can save $8 per week. Which equation can be used to find x, the number of weeks she will have to save in order to buy the CD player?

A $8x = 64 + 96$

B $8x + 64 = 96$

C $8x - 64 = 96$

D $8x \div 64 = 96$

9 Solve: $7a - 5a + 15 = 45$

$a = ?$

10 Solve: $3a + a - 11 > 9$

A $a > -5$

B $a < -5$

C $a > 5$

D $a < 5$

11 What is a mathematical sentence for the following?

2.5 more than the product of a number and 3 is greater than 7.5.

A $2.5 + (n + 3) > 7.5$

B $2.5 > 3n + 7.5$

C $2.5 + 3n < 7.5$

D $2.5 + 3n > 7.5$

12 The solution of which inequality is graphed below?

A $x \geq -2$

B $x > -2$

C $x < -2$

D $x \leq -2$

13 Which equation is equivalent to $3n + 5n - 27 = 45$?

A $n = 8$

B $8n = 18$

C $8n = 72$

D $9n = 72$

Go On ➡

14 What is the amount of simple interest for an investment of $300 invested for 3 years at a rate of 4%?
(Use the formula $i = prt$.)

A $12

B $18

C $36

D $360

15 Which linear equation has this graph?

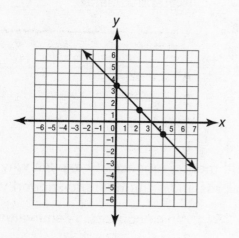

A $y = x + 3$

B $y = x - 3$

C $y = 3x$

D $y = -x + 3$

16 What is the slope of this line?

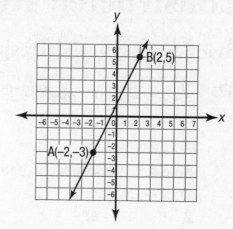

A $\dfrac{2}{1}$

B $-\dfrac{2}{1}$

C $\dfrac{3}{1}$

D $-\dfrac{3}{1}$

STOP

Standard 1.0: Algebra, Patterns, or Functions

Constructed Response Questions

Brief Constructed Response

17 This is an arithmetic sequence:

  −4, −1, 2, 5,...

Step A What is the eighth term in this sequence?

_____

Step B Use what you know about arithmetic sequences to explain why your answer is correct. Use words and/or numbers to support your explanation.

_____

_____

_____

_____

Go On ➡

18 This expression gives the area of a rectangle:

$(x - 4)(2x - 3)$

Step A What is the value of the expression when $x = 8$?

_____

Sep B Use what you know about evaluating expressions and the order of operations to explain why your answer is correct. Use words and/or numbers to support your explanation.

_____

_____

_____

_____

_____

Go On ➥

Extended Constructed Response

19   A line has the equation $2x + y = 5$.

Step A   List three ordered pairs that are solutions of the equation.

_____

_____

Step B   • Use what you know about finding ordered pair solutions to explain why your answer is correct. Use words and/or numbers to support your explanation.

_____

_____

   • Graph the ordered pairs on the coordinate grid below and draw a line through the points. What is the slope of the line? Use what you know about finding the slope of a line to explain why your answer is correct.

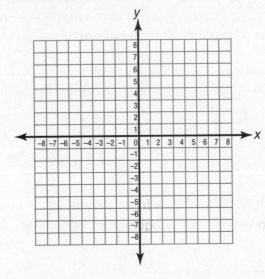

_____

_____

Go On ➡

20 A taxi charges a flat fee of $6 plus $2.50 per mile. Corey took the taxi and paid $16, not including tip.

Step A Write an equation that can be used to find *m*, the number of miles Corey traveled in the taxi.

_____

Step B • Use what you know about writing equations to explain why your answer is correct. Use words and/or numbers to support your explanation.

_____

_____

_____

• Solve the equation step by step to find the number of miles in Corey's trip. Use what you know about solving equations to explain why your solution is correct.

_____

_____

_____

• Choose two equations from your step-by-step solution and explain why they are equivalent equations.

_____

_____

_____

Go On ➡

21 Ben wrote this inequality to solve a problem:

$$2n - 1.75 < 4.25$$

Step A   Solve the inequality.

_____

Step B   • Use what you know about solving inequalities to explain why your answer is correct. Use words and/or numbers to support your explanation.

_____

_____

_____

• Graph the inequality on the number line below. Use what you know about graphing inequalities to explain why your graph is correct.

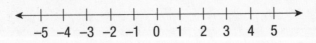

_____

_____

_____

In this unit you will learn some concepts from geometry. You will learn that when two parallel lines are both intersected by a third line, the angles formed have special relationships.

Try This

You will need:

- a partner
- lined paper
- a ruler
- a protractor

Follow these steps:

1. Each partner uses a sheet of lined paper to draw parallel lines *a* and *b*, and another line *c* that intersects both lines *a* and *b*. Each line you draw should be at least 5 inches long. Your line *c* should not cross lines *a* and *b* at the same angles as the one in the drawing below. The way you number your angles, however, should match the way the angles are numbered in the drawing.

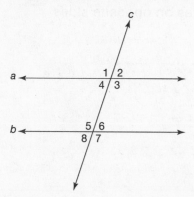

2. Use a protractor to measure each angle in your drawing and record its measure.

3. Use your results to complete each statement:

   Angle 1 and angle 3 are _____   Angle 1 and angle 5 are _____

   Angle 3 and angle 5 are _____   Angle 3 and angle 6 are _____

   Angle 3 and angle 7 are _____   Angle 1 and angle 7 are _____

4. Compare your completed statements with your partner's. Discuss any differences in the way you completed the statements.

Think about it:

How many different angle measures did you find? What patterns do you see in your and your partner's completed statements?

LESSON

12 Angles Formed by Parallel Lines and Transversals

When two parallel lines are intersected by a third line, there are three theorems about angles that you need to know.

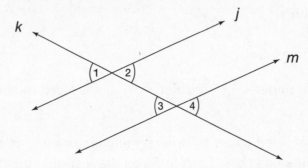

In the diagram, the parallel lines are *j* and *m*; the intersecting line is *k*. This intersecting line is called a transversal. Angles marked 2 and 3 are alternate interior angles. Angles marked 1 and 3 are corresponding angles, and angles marked 1 and 4 are alternate exterior angles. The word "alternate" refers to angles on opposite sides of the transversal.

Theorem 1	Alternate interior angles are congruent: $\angle 2 \cong \angle 3$
Theorem 2	Corresponding angles are congruent: $\angle 1 \cong \angle 3$
Theorem 3	Alternate exterior angles are congruent: $\angle 1 \cong \angle 4$

Example 1

In the diagram below lines *m* and *n* are parallel lines. Line *q* is a transversal. What is the name of the pair of angles marked *a* and *b*?

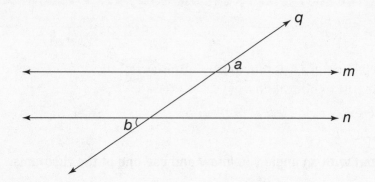

STRATEGY: Use the definitions at the beginning of the lesson.

STEP 1: Are angles a and b on the same side or opposite sides of the transversal *q*?

They are on opposite sides of the transversal *q*.

STEP 2: Are angles *a* and *b* inside or outside of the parallel lines *m* and *n*?

They are outside of the parallel lines.

STEP 3: Put together the information from Steps 1 and 2 to name the angles *a* and *b*.

SOLUTION: The angles *a* and *b* are called alternate exterior angles.

Example 2

In this figure, lines *s* and *n* are parallel and line *t* is a transversal. Find the measure of $\angle x$.

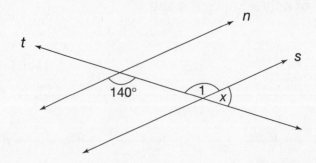

STRATEGY: **Start with an angle you know and use one of the theorems.**

STEP 1: What angle is known?

One interior angle is known—it measures 140°.

STEP 2: Find the measure of $\angle 1$.

$\angle 1$ is an alternate interior angle to the angle whose measure is 140°.

So the measure of $\angle 1 = 140°$ (Theorem 1).

STEP 3: Find the measure of $\angle x$.

Since $\angle 1$ and $\angle x$ form a straight line, they are supplementary.

The sum of the measures of $\angle 1$ and $\angle x$ is 180°.

$140 + x = 180$

SOLUTION: $x = 40°$

Sample Test Questions

1 Line *p* is parallel to line *q*. Which answer shows accurate angle relationships?

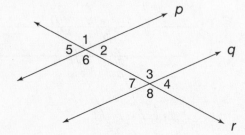

A ∠1 ≅ ∠3; ∠6 ≅ ∠7

B ∠1 ≅ ∠3; ∠6 ≅ ∠8

C ∠5 ≅ ∠7; ∠2 ≅ ∠3

D ∠5 ≅ ∠3; ∠1 ≅ ∠8

2 Line *m* is parallel to line *n*. Which answer shows accurate angle relationships?

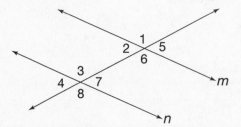

A ∠6 ≅ ∠7; ∠2 ≅ ∠7

B ∠6 ≅ ∠3; ∠2 ≅ ∠3

C ∠6 ≅ ∠3; ∠2 ≅ ∠8

D ∠6 ≅ ∠3; ∠2 ≅ ∠7

3 Line *r* is parallel to line *s*. Which answer shows accurate angle relationships?

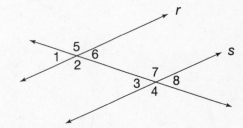

A ∠5 ≅ ∠4; ∠1 ≅ ∠8

B ∠5 ≅ ∠7; ∠1 ≅ ∠7

C ∠4 ≅ ∠6; ∠4 ≅ ∠5

D ∠4 ≅ ∠5; ∠8 ≅ ∠2

4 In the figure, lines k_1 and k_2 are parallel, and lines m_1 and m_2 are parallel. What is the measure of ∠*x*?

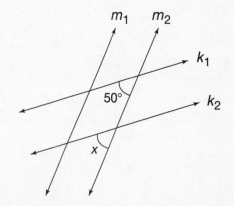

A 40°

B 50°

C 60°

D 70°

Go On ➡

5 Lines m_1 and m_2 are parallel. Which angle measures 47°?

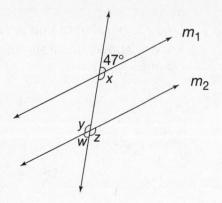

A w

B x

C y

D z

6 Name all congruent angles to $\angle a$ in the figure below, where l_1 is parallel to l_2 and l_3 is parallel to l_4.

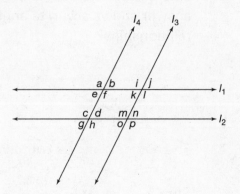

A f, i, c, h, b, d

B f, i, l, c, h, m, p

C g, k, j, n, o, d

D b, e, f, c, d, g, h

Go On ➡

Extended Constructed Response

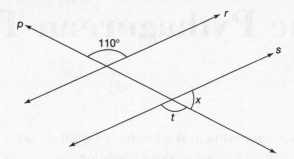

7 The diagram shows two parallel lines *r* and *s* and transversal *p*.

Step A   Find the measure of angle *t*.

Step B
- Use what you know about transversals intersecting parallel lines to justify your answer. Use words and diagrams to support your justification.

_____

_____

_____

- Find the measure of angle *x*. Explain how you got your answer.

_____

_____

_____

LESSON 13

The Pythagorean Theorem

One of the most famous theorems in the history of mathematics is the Pythagorean Theorem. It has to do with the sides of right triangles:

The Pythagorean Theorem

In any right triangle, the square of the length of the hypotenuse is equal to the sum of the squares of the lengths of the legs.

The **hypotenuse** is the side opposite the right angle. It is always the longest side of a right triangle. The two shorter sides that form the right angle are called **legs**.

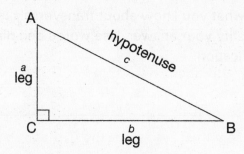

Written as a formula, the Pythagorean Theorem is:

$$a^2 + b^2 = c^2$$

You will often use this formula to solve problems.

Example

Tanya's TV screen measures 20 inches in length. The width is 15 inches. The size of a TV screen is measured by the length of the diagonal. What is the size of Tanya's TV screen?

STRATEGY: **Use the formula for the Pythagorean Theorem.**

STEP 1:   Draw a diagram.

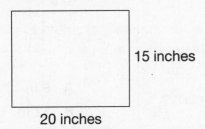

15 inches

20 inches

STEP 2:   Highlight the 2 legs and the hypotenuse of the right triangle in the diagram.

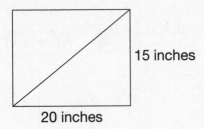

15 inches

20 inches

STEP 3:   Apply the formula for the Pythagorean Theorem.

Substitute the lengths of the two legs in this formula:

$a^2 + b^2 = c^2$

$a = 20$, $b = 15$, $c = ?$

$20^2 + 15^2 = c^2$

STEP 4:   Compute the answer.

$20^2 = 400$ and $15^2 = 225$

So, $c^2 = 400 + 225 = 625$

$c = \sqrt{625} = 25$

SOLUTION: **The length of the diagonal is 25 inches (the size of the TV).**

SPECIAL NOTE: The triangle in the Example is part of an important group of triangles called *3-4-5 right triangles*. The lengths of the legs are multiples of the numbers 3 and 4, and the hypotenuse is a multiple of 5.

Sample Test Questions

1 Which of the following represents the hypotenuse *q*?

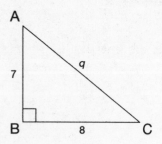

A $\sqrt{8^2} + \sqrt{7^2}$

B $\sqrt{8^2 - 7^2}$

C $\sqrt{8^2 + 7^2}$

D $8^2 + 7^2$

2 What is the length of leg *p*?

A $\sqrt{9^2 - 4^2}$

B $\sqrt{9^2 + 4^2}$

C $9^2 + 4^2$

D $\dfrac{9^2 + 4^2}{2}$

3 What is *x*?

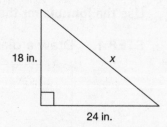

A 6 in.

B 12 in.

C 30 in.

D 36 in.

4 What is *x*?

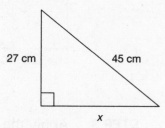

A 18 cm

B 20 cm

C 24 cm

D 36 cm

Go On ➡

Brief Constructed Response

5 A new park was just completed in the village of Hendrick. It is in the form of a rectangle. The length and the width of the park along with the diagonal of the park form a 3-4-5 right triangle.

Step A If the diagonal of the park is 500 meters, what is the length of the sides of the park?

_____

Step B Use your knowledge of the Pythagorean Theorem and 3-4-5 right triangles to justify why your answer is correct. Use diagrams and words to support your justification.

_____

_____

_____

_____

STOP

LESSON

Standards 2.C.1.a, b, c

14 Special Constructions

This lesson will show you how to draw three different types of constructions using rulers and compasses.

1. Drawing Quadrilaterals

In Example 1, follow how a quadrilateral is drawn given the dimensions of its sides. No angle measures are given. In Example 2, you will see how to draw a quadrilateral with two angles given and two sides given.

Example 1

Drawing a Quadrilateral With Four Given Sides

Draw quadrilateral *ABCD* with $\overline{AB}$ = 3 cm, $\overline{BC}$ = 4 cm, $\overline{CD}$ = 5 cm, and $\overline{AD}$ = 6 cm.

STRATEGY: **Measure and draw two consecutive sides without using a compass, then use a compass to measure the other two sides.**

STEP 1: Draw sides $\overline{AB}$ and $\overline{BC}$. You do not need to measure ∠*ABC*.

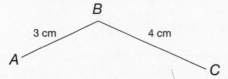

STEP 2: Measure a compass opening of 5 cm.

STEP 3: Place your compass point at *A* and draw an arc toward the interior of the quadrilateral.

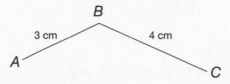

STEP 4: Measure a compass opening of 6 cm.

STEP 5: Place your compass point at *C* and draw an arc towards the interior of the quadrilateral, intersecting the arc drawn in Step 3.

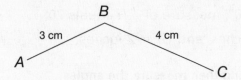

STEP 6: Connect *A* and *C* with the point of intersection of the two arcs. Mark the intersecting point *D*.

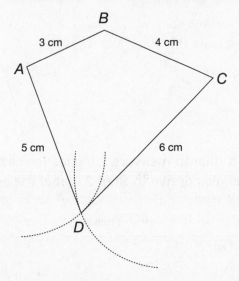

SOLUTION: The quadrilateral *ABCD* above is the desired quadrilateral with sides equal to 3 cm, 4 cm, 5 cm, and 6 cm.

Example 2

Drawing a Quadrilateral with Three Given Sides and Two Given Angles

Draw Quadrilateral *FGHJ* with these specifications:

Measure of ∠*G* equals 60°; measure of ∠*H* equals 70°

GH = 3 inches, *HJ* = 2 inches, and *GF* = 2 inches.

STRATEGY: **Draw *GH* first and then measure the angles.**

STEP 1: Use a ruler to draw segment *GH* 3 inches long.

3 inches
G ——————————————————— H

STEP 2: Use a protractor to measure an angle of 60° with vertex *G*, and a second angle of 70° with vertex *H*.

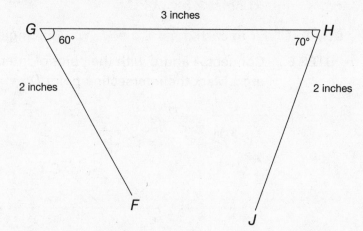

STEP 3:

Use a ruler to measure 2 inches for each of the two sides of the angles drawn in Step 2. Label the endpoints of the sides *F* and *J*.

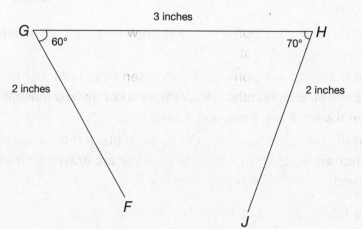

STEP 4: Draw segment *FJ*.

SOLUTION: Quadrilateral *FGHJ* has the required specifications.

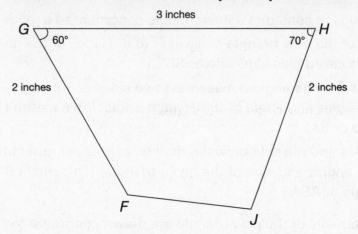

2. Constructing a Perpendicular through a Given Point on a Line Segment

Given: Segment *JK* and any point *Z* on $\overline{JK}$.

Two lines are **perpendicular** to each other if they form right angles with each other.

Draw a line *PZ* that is perpendicular to a given line *JK*.

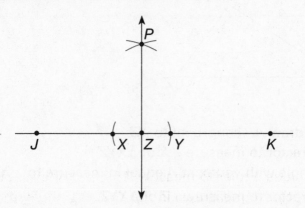

Follow these steps:

1   Place the compass point at *Z* and draw two arcs to the left and right of *Z*, intersecting the line at *X* and *Y*.

2   Place the compass point at *X* and extend the radius of the arc (open up the compass slightly) so that the compass radius is greater than *ZX*. Draw an arc above the line.

3   Without changing the compass setting, place the compass point at *Y*. Draw another arc so that it intersects with the arc drawn from *X*. The point of intersection of the two arcs is point *P*.

4   Draw $\overleftrightarrow{PZ}$. This line is perpendicular to $\overline{JK}$.

3. Constructing a Triangle Congruent to a Given Triangle

There are three methods to construct a new triangle congruent to a given triangle:

1   Draw all sides of the new triangle congruent to the sides of the given triangle. (This method is called side-side-side or SSS.)

2   Draw two sides and the angle between the two sides congruent to two corresponding sides and angle of the given triangle. (This method is called side-angle-side or SAS.)

3   Draw two angles and the side between the two angles congruent to two corresponding angles and side of the given triangle. (This method is called angle-side-angle or ASA.)

In each case, three elements of the new triangle are drawn congruent to corresponding elements of the given triangle. The steps below outline method number 2. You will get a chance to construct a congruent triangle using method number 3 in the Constructed Response Questions at the end of this lesson.

Constructing a Triangle Congruent to a Given Triangle Using SAS: Method 2

Given *XYZ*

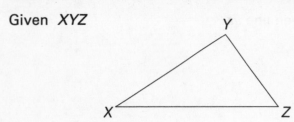

Follow these steps:

1   Use a ruler to draw $\overline{AB}$ congruent to $\overline{XZ}$.
2   Use your protractor to measure $\angle X$ of $\triangle XYZ$.
3   Measure an angle with vertex at A equal in measure to $\angle X$.
4   Use your protractor to measure $\angle Z$ of $\triangle XYZ$.
5   Measure an angle with vertex at B equal in measure to $\angle Z$.
6   Extend the sides of $\angle A$ and $\angle B$ until they intersect in point C.

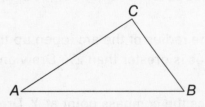

Triangle *ABC* is congruent to triangle *XYZ*.

Brief Constructed Response

1 Corey challenges his friend Marc to construct a perpendicular to a segment.

Step A Here is the segment. Draw a perpendicular to this segment at point Q.

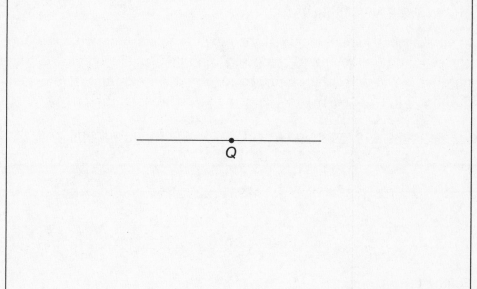

Step B Use what you know about constructing a perpendicular to a segment at a point to explain why your construction is correct.

_____

_____

_____

_____

Go On ➡

2   Monty wants to know how to draw a triangle congruent to a given triangle.

Step A

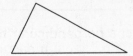

Here is a triangle. Use a protractor and a ruler to draw a triangle congruent to this one by the ASA method. (See page 88.)

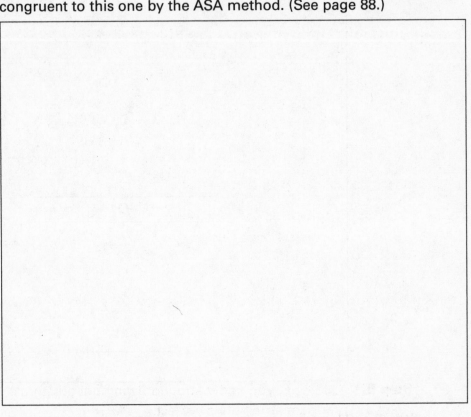

Step B   Use what you know about congruent triangles to explain why your construction is correct.

3 Yasir says he knows the lengths of three sides of a quadrilateral and he knows the measure of one angle. Now he wants to know how to draw the quadrilateral.

Step A Draw a quadrilateral with these specifications: two sides equal to 8 cm, one side equal to 10 cm, and an angle measuring 40°.

Step B Use what you know about drawing quadrilaterals to explain why your construction is correct.

_____

_____

_____

_____

LESSON

15 Similar Polygons

Standard 2.D.1.a

Two figures are similar if they have the same shape.

If two figures are similar, then the following two properties are true:

1 The angles of one figure are congruent to the corresponding angles of the second figure.

2 The corresponding sides of the two figures are proportional.

Example 1

If hexagon *ABCDEF* is similar to hexagon *PQRSTV*, what is the length of $\overline{RS}$?

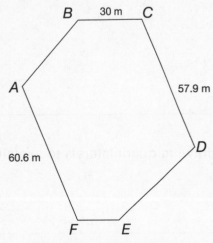
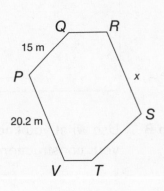

STRATEGY: **Find the ratio of the lengths of two corresponding sides of the hexagons and use a proportion.**

STEP 1: From the diagram, find the lengths of two corresponding sides.

The two corresponding sides whose lengths are shown are $\overline{AF}$ and $\overline{PV}$. Their lengths are 60.6 cm and 20.2 cm.

These sides are the only corresponding sides with lengths that are shown.

92

STEP 2: Find the ratio of the lengths of the two corresponding sides. (This is sometimes called the **scale factor**.)

$$\frac{AF}{PV} = \frac{60.6}{20.2}$$

STEP 3: Simplify the ratio $\frac{60.6}{20.2}$.

$$\frac{AF}{PV} = \frac{60.6}{20.2} = \frac{3}{1}$$

STEP 4: Form a proportion using corresponding sides to find *RS*.

$$\frac{AF}{PV} = \frac{CD}{RS}$$

STEP 5: Use the ratio $\frac{3}{1}$ for $\frac{AF}{PV}$ in the proportion of Step 4, substitute for *CD*, and solve for $\overline{RS}$.

The proportion $\frac{AF}{PV} = \frac{CD}{RS}$ becomes $\frac{3}{1} = \frac{57.9}{x}$

Cross multiply: $3x = 57.9$

$$x = 19.3$$

SOLUTION: **The length of side $\overline{RS}$ is 19.3 meters.**

Example 2

Pentagon *GHJKL* is similar to pentagon *VWXYZ*. Find the measure of $\angle Z$.

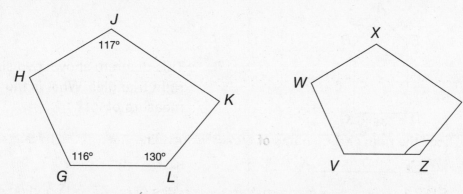

STRATEGY: **Use the fact that corresponding angles of similar figures are congruent.**

STEP 1: Find the angle that corresponds to $\angle Z$.

The angle corresponding to $\angle Z$ is $\angle L$.

STEP 2: What is the measure of $\angle L$?

The measure of $\angle L$ is 130°.

SOLUTION: **So the measure of $\angle Z$ is 130°.**

Sample Test Questions

1 △*PQR* is similar to △*XYZ*. What is the length of $\overline{YZ}$?

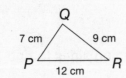
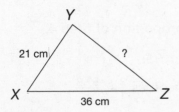

A 20 cm   **C** 27 cm

B 24 cm   **D** 30 cm

2 Pentagon *ABCDE* is similar to pentagon *VWXYZ*. What is the length of segment $\overline{ZY}$?

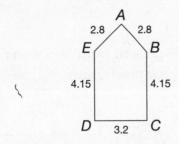

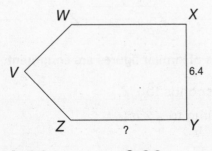

A 6.3   **C** 8.3

B 7.3   **D** 8.55

3 Quadrilateral *ABCD* is similar to quadrilateral *TUVW*. What is the sum of the measures of ∠*T* and ∠*V*?

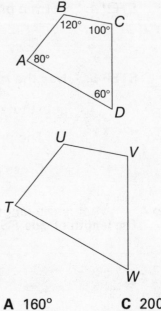

A 160°   **C** 200°

B 180°   **D** 220°

4 This diagram shows two similar right triangles. What is the measure of ∠*L*?

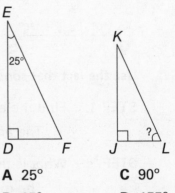

A 25°   **C** 90°

B 65°   **D** 155°

Go On ➡

94

Brief Constructed Response

5   Maggie wants to compare the lengths of two similar rectangular frames.

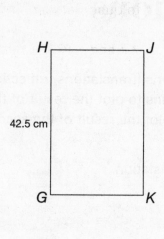

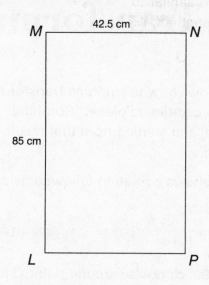

Step A   What is the length of side $\overline{HJ}$ of the frame *GHJK*?

_____

Step B   Use what you know about similar polygons to justify your answer.
Use words and diagrams to support your justification.

_____

_____

_____

_____

STOP

Standard 2.E.1.a

LESSON 16
Combining Transformations

This lesson shows how to combine transformations (translations, reflections, and rotations) on a coordinate plane. "Combine" means to plot the result of the first transformation, and starting from that result, to plot the result of the second transformation.

This example shows a rotation followed by a translation.

Example 1

Rotate △PQR 90° clockwise around point Q followed by a translation of 3 units down. What is the set of coordinates for the vertices of the triangle after the two transformations?

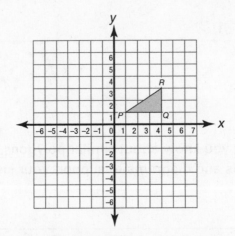

STRATEGY: Rotate the triangle first, then translate the result.

Rotation of triangle 90° clockwise around point Q

STEP 1: Start with point Q.

Since point Q is the point of rotation, it remains in the same location (4,1) after the 90° rotation.

STEP 2: What happens to point P after a 90° clockwise rotation?

Point P is located at (1,1).

After a clockwise rotation of 90°, P moves to (4,4).

96

STEP 3: What happens to point *R* after a 90° clockwise rotation?

Point *R* is located at (4,3).

After the clockwise rotation of 90°, *R* moves to (6,1).

The coordinates for the triangle after the 90° rotation are (4,1), (4,4), and (6,1).

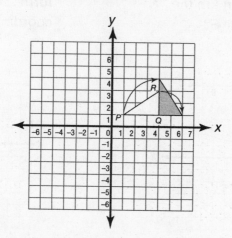

Translation of rotated triangle 3 units down.

STEP 4: What changes take place to the *x* and *y* coordinates of any point if the point gets translated 3 units down?

There is no change to the *x*-coordinate. The *y*-coordinate is reduced by 3.

STEP 5: What are the coordinates of the vertices of the triangle after the translation of 3 units down?

After the translation, the triangle looks like this:

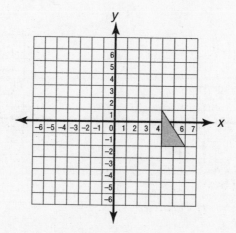

SOLUTION: The vertices of the triangle after the translation are (4,−2), (4,1), and (6,−2).

Sample Test Questions

1 △*ABC* is translated 4 units to the left to form △*DEF*, and then △*DEF* is reflected over the *x*-axis to form △*GHJ*. What are the coordinates of point *G*?

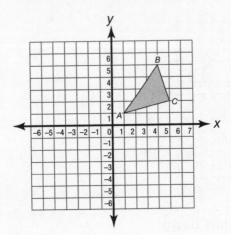

A (−3,1)   C (−2,−1)
B (−3,−1)   D (−2,1)

2 △*JKL* is rotated 90° clockwise around point L to form △*ABC*, and then △*ABC* is reflected over the *x*-axis to form △*DEF*. What are the coordinates of point *E*?

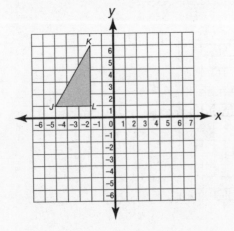

A (−2,1)   C (3,−3)
B (−2,4)   D (3,−1)

3 △*JKL* is reflected over the *x*-axis to form △*MNP*, and then △*MNP* is reflected over the *y*-axis to form △*QRS*. What are the coordinates of point *S*?

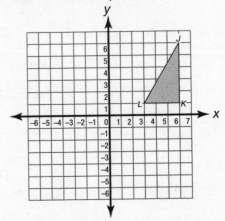

A (3,−1)   C (−3,−2)
B (−3,1)   D (−3,−1)

4 △*XYZ* is rotated 180° counter-clockwise around point X to form △*LMN*, and then △*LMN* is translated down 2 to form △*PQR*. What are the coordinates of point *P*?

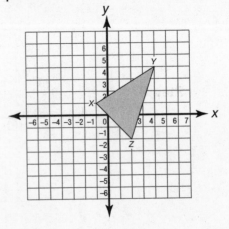

A (1,−1)   C (1,1)
B (−1,−1)   D (−1,1)

98

Go On ➡

Brief Constructed Response

5   Omar plotted △*XYZ* on a coordinate plane. See the diagram below.

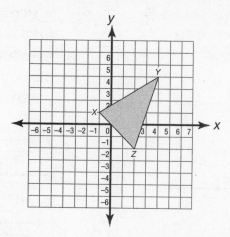

Step A   On this coordinate plane, draw △*ABC* that results after △*XYZ* is translated 4 units to the left. Then reflect △*ABC* over the *x*-axis to form △*DEF*. Draw △*DEF*.

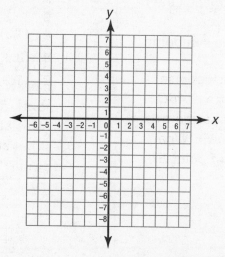

Step B   Use what you know about transformations to explain why your result is correct. Use words and diagrams in your explanation.

_____

_____

STOP

Standard 2.0: Geometry

Progress Check for Lessons 12–16

1 What is *x*?

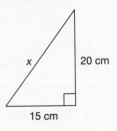

x   20 cm

15 cm

A 24 cm

B 25 cm

C 27 cm

D 30 cm

2 Lines *p* and *q* are parallel. Line *z* is a transversal. Find *x*. (Disregard the degree symbol in your answer.)

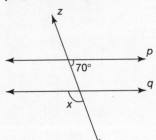

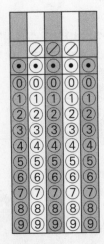

3 △*XYZ* is reflected over the *x*-axis to form △*UVW*, followed by a translation of △*UVW* 2 units to the right to form △*RST*. What are the coordinates of point *T*?

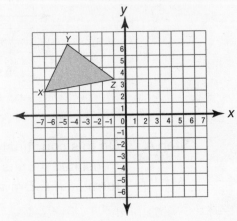

A (1,3)

B (3,−1)

C (1,−3)

D (1,−2)

Go On ➡

100

4 Which one of these methods is NOT a method for constructing one triangle congruent to a given triangle.

A Draw all sides of the new triangle congruent to the sides of the given triangle.

B Draw all angles of the new triangle congruent to the angles of the given triangle.

C Draw two sides and the angle between the two sides congruent to two corresponding sides and angle of the given triangle.

D Draw two angles and the side between the two angles congruent to two corresponding angles and side of the given triangle.

5 Pentagon *ABCDE* is similar to pentagon *FGHJK*. What is the length of side *GH*?

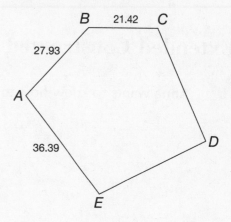

A 7.14

B 14.28

C 42.84

D 64.26

Go On ➡

Standard 2.0: Geometry

Constructed Response Questions

Extended Constructed Response

6 Anna wants to know how to construct a triangle congruent to this one.

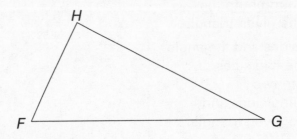

Step A Construct a triangle congruent to △*FGH*

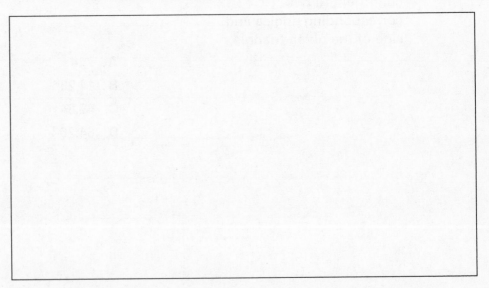

Step B • Use what you know about drawing a triangle congruent to a given triangle to explain why your construction is correct. Use words and/or diagrams to support your answer.

_____

_____

_____

Go On ➡

102

- Construct a second triangle congruent to the given triangle using a different method and explain why you think this triangle is also congruent to the given triangle. Use words and/or diagrams to support your answer.

Measurement

In this unit you will learn about measurement. The areas of composite figures are easier to find if you can divide the figure into polygons whose area formulas you know.

Try This

You will need:

- a partner
- a ruler

Follow these steps:

1. In the composite figure below, dashed lines are used to divide the figure into polygons whose areas are easy to find.

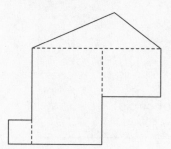

2. Create two copies of your own composite figure using rectangles, squares, and/or triangles. Use no more than 6 polygons. On one copy show the polygons you used. On the other, just show the outline of the figure.

3. Exchange copies of the outlined composite figure with your partner. Use a pencil and a ruler to draw in the polygons you think were used to create the figure.

4. Compare the results to the original figures showing the polygons that were used. Did your partner use exactly the same polygons you did? Discuss any differences.

Think about it:

How many different ways could your composite figure be divided into polygons?

Do some of the ways make finding the area easier than others?

LESSON 17 Circle Relationships

Study these relationships among the different parts of a circle.

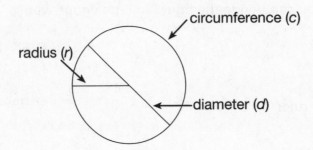

•	**Radius and Diameter**	$d = 2r$
•	**Circumference and Diameter**	$c = \pi d$
•	**Circumference and Radius** From the two formulas above:	$c = 2\pi r$
•	**Radius and Area**	$A = \pi r^2$ (A = area of circle)

What is π? It is an important number in mathematics. One way to think of π is to think of it as the ratio of the circumference to the diameter of any circle.

$$\pi = \frac{c}{d}$$

Two good approximations of the irrational number π are $\frac{22}{7}$ and 3.14.

Example 1

The park in the middle of Jackson City is in the shape of a circle. The diameter is 4,609 ft. Find the circumference of the park to the nearest whole foot.

STRATEGY: **Use the formula with the circumference and diameter above.**

STEP 1: What formula will you use?

The best formula to use is $c = \pi d$

STEP 2: Substitute the diameter of the park in the formula of Step 1.

$c = \pi \times 4{,}609$

STEP 3: Use $\pi = 3.14$ to compute the circumference.

$c = \pi \times 4{,}609 = 3.14 \times 4{,}609 = 14{,}472.26$

STEP 4: Round 14,472.26 to the nearest whole number.

14,472.26 rounded to the nearest whole number is 14,472.

SOLUTION: **The circumference of the park is 14,472 ft.**

Example 2

Find the area of a circle whose circumference is 31.4 cm.

STRATEGY: **Use the formulas to find the radius and then the area.**

STEP 1: Find the radius.

Use the formula for circumference and radius: $c = 2\pi r$

$31.4 = 2\pi r$

Substitute 3.14 for π.

$31.4 = 2 \times 3.14 r$

$31.4 = 6.28 r$

Solve for r.

$r = 5$ cm

STEP 2: Find the area.

Use the formula $A = \pi r^2$ and substitute π and r.

$A = 3.14 \times 5^2 = 3.14 \times 25 = 78.5$ sq. cm

SOLUTION: **The area of the circle is 78.5 sq. cm.**

Sample Test Questions

Use π = 3.14.

1 Find the circumference of a circle with a radius of 3,000 m.

A 6,000 m

B 9,420 m

C 16,840 m

D 18,840 m

2 Find the area to the nearest two decimal places of a circle with a radius equal to 4.52 cm.

A 14.19 cm^2

B 64.15 cm^2

C 128.3 cm^2

D 256.61 cm^2

3 Find the area of a circle with a diameter equal to 10 in.

A 314 sq. in.

B 78.5 sq. in.

C 19.625 sq. in.

D 10.625 sq. in.

4 The circumference of a circle is 62.8 mm; what is the radius?

Go On ➡

Brief Constructed Response

5 Maria drew a circle on the ground using chalk on one end of a rope. When she finished she measured the diameter. It was 6 ft.

Step A What is the area of the circle?

_____

Step B Use what you know about finding the area of circles to explain why your answer is correct. Use words and/or numbers in your explanation.

_____

_____

_____

_____

_____

18 Area of Composite Figures

A composite figure is made up of other figures. In this lesson composite figures will consist only of rectangles and triangles.

Example 1

Find the area of this figure.

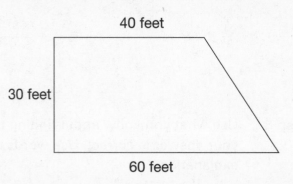

STRATEGY: Divide the figure into smaller figures and calculate the area of each figure.

STEP 1: Draw a dotted segment to show the figure divided into a rectangle and a triangle.

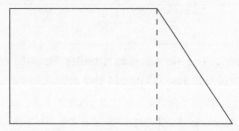

STEP 2: What are the length and width of the rectangle?

The length of the rectangle is 40 ft and the width is 30 ft.

STEP 3: Find the area of the rectangle.

Substitute in the formula: $A = l \times w$

$A = 40 \times 30 = 1,200$ sq ft

STEP 4: What are the base and height of the triangle?

The triangle is a right triangle, so the base is $60 - 40 = 20$ ft.

The height of the triangle is 30 ft.

110

STEP 5:   Find the area of the triangle.
Substitute in the formula: $A = \frac{1}{2}b \times h$
$A = \frac{1}{2} \times 20 \times 30 = 300$ sq ft

STEP 6:   Add the areas of the rectangle and the triangle.
$1,200 + 300 = 1,500$ sq ft

SOLUTION: **The area of the composite figure is 1,500 sq ft.**

Example 2

This is a sketch of a park in the back of McHenry School. The scale for this sketch is 1 cm 5 10 ft. Find the area of the park.

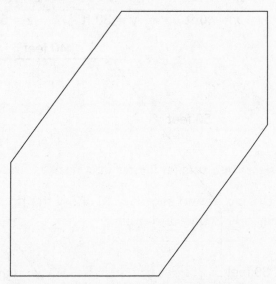

STRATEGY: **Divide the figure of the sketch into smaller figures, measure the dimensions of the smaller figures, and compute the area of each.**

STEP 1:   Divide the figure on the sketch into smaller figures so that the area of each figure can be computed.

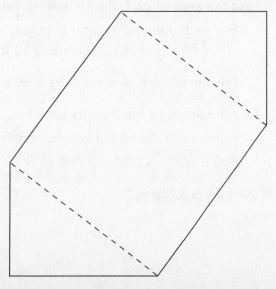

The original figure of the sketch was subdivided into three figures—two congruent right triangles and a square.

111

STEP 2: Use a centimeter ruler to measure the sides of the original figure of the sketch.

The legs of the two right triangles measure 3 cm and 4 cm. The side of the square is 5 cm.

STEP 3: Use the scale to find the actual dimensions of the park.

The scale is 1 cm = 10 ft

To find the actual dimensions of the park, set up proportions and solve them:

Use variables x and y for the legs of the right triangle, and z for the width of the rectangle.

$$\frac{1}{10} = \frac{4}{x} \qquad \frac{1}{10} = \frac{3}{y} \qquad \frac{1}{10} = \frac{5}{z}$$

$$x = 40 \text{ ft} \qquad y = 30 \text{ ft} \qquad z = 50 \text{ ft}$$

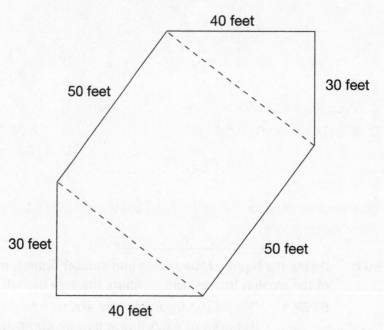

STEP 4: Find the area of each figure that makes up the original sketch.

For each congruent right triangle:
$A = \frac{1}{2}bh = \frac{1}{2} \times 40 \times 30 = 600$ sq ft

For the square, $A = bh = 50 \times 50 = 2{,}500$ sq ft

STEP 5: Add the areas of the figures together.

Remember, there are two congruent triangles.

$600 + 600 + 2{,}500 = 3{,}700$ sq ft

SOLUTION: **The area of the park is 3,700 sq ft.**

Sample Test Questions

1 This figure can be subdivided into several figures. Which combination is possible?

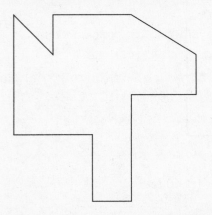

A 2 rectangles and 2 triangles

B 3 rectangles and 2 triangles

C 4 rectangles and 2 triangles

D 4 rectangle and 3 triangles

2 This is the same figure as in Question 1. What is the area of the figure?

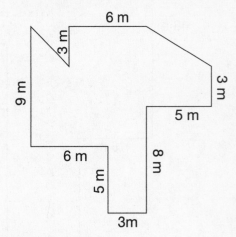

A 112.5 sq m

B 114 sq m

C 118 sq m

D 120.5 sq m

3 Use your centimeter ruler to measure the dimensions, and find the area of the composite figure.

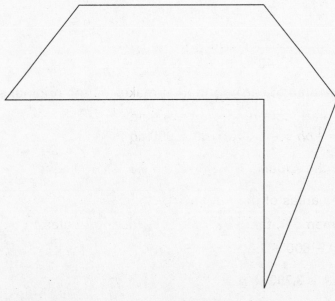

A 20.5 sq cm

C 22 sq cm

B 21.5 sq cm

D 22.5 sq cm

Go On ➡

113

4 Find the area (in sq m) of this composite figure.

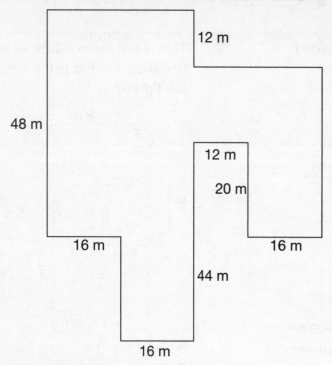

12 m

48 m

12 m

20 m

16 m

16 m

44 m

16 m

Go On ➡

Brief Constructed Response

5 Pierre challenged his friend Jose to find the area of this figure.

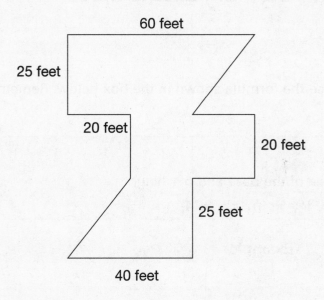

Step A Find the area of Pierre's figure.

_____

Step B Use what you know about finding the area of composite figures to explain why your answer is correct. Use words and/or diagrams to support your answer.

_____

_____

_____

_____

LESSON 19 Volume of Cylinders

To find the volume of a cylinder use the formula shown in the box below. Remember, the base of a cylinder is a circle.

> $V = Bh$
>
> where B = area of the base and h = height
>
> Since $B = \pi r^2$, $V = \pi r^2 h$. (π = 3.14)

Example

Find the volume of this cylinder.

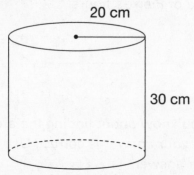

20 cm

30 cm

STRATEGY: Use the formula for finding the volume of a cylinder.

STEP 1: Write the formula for finding the volume.

$V = \pi r^2 h$

STEP 2: Find the values of r and h from the diagram.

From the diagram, $r = 20$ cm and $h = 30$ cm.

STEP 3: Substitute for π, r, and h in the formula. Use $\pi = 3.14$.

$V = \pi r^2 h = 3.14 \times (20)^2 \times 30$

STEP 4: Do the math.

$V = 3.14 \times (20)^2 \times 30 = 37,680$ cu cm

SOLUTION: The volume of the cylinder is 37,680 cu cm.

Sample Test Questions

1 Find the volume of a cylinder with base radius equal to 10 cm and height equal to 20 cm. (Use 3.14 for π.)

A 6,280 cu cm

B 3,140 cu cm

C 1,256 cu cm

D 628 cu cm

2 Find the volume of a cylinder with a base diameter of 10 in. and a height of 20 in.

A 6,280 cu in.

B 4,280 cu in.

C 3,280 cu in.

D 1,570 cu in.

3 What is the volume, to the nearest tenth, of a cylinder with radius equal to 12.5 cm and height equal to 17.5 cm?

A 31,651.2 cm^3

B 17,171.9 cm^3

C 15,825.6 cm^3

D 8,585.9 cm^3

4 Find the height of a cylinder whose volume is 6908 cubic units and whose base radius is 10 units. (Use $\pi = 3.14$.)

A 33 units

B 24 units

C 22 units

D 11 units

Go On ➡

Brief Constructed Response

5 Desiree has a fish tank that is in the shape of a rectangular prism. The dimensions of the tank are 20 inches long by 10 inches wide by 8 inches high.

Step A After she empties the tank, she fills it with water using a cylindrical flask that has a diameter of 4 inches and height of 6 inches. How many flasks full of water does she have to use to fill the tank?

_____

Step B Use what you know about finding the volume of cylinders to explain why your answer is correct. Use words and/or diagrams to support your answer.

_____

_____

_____

_____

LESSON 20

Solving Problems Using Proportions and Rates

Scale Drawings and Proportions

Scale drawings and scale models can show objects that may be very big, or very small, or very complex. Common examples of scale drawings and scale models are maps, architects' drawings, and models of homes and buildings.

In all cases a numerical scale is used to compute the actual dimensions. A scale is a ratio—the ratio between the dimensions of the drawing and the actual dimensions of the object.

Example 1

On a map, Andy measured the distance between Baltimore and Hagerstown. It is 9 cm. The scale on the map shows 4 cm = 30 miles. What is the approximate distance from Baltimore to Hagerstown?

STRATEGY: **Write a proportion and solve it.**

STEP 1: Use the scale to set up the proportion.

$$\frac{4 \text{ cm}}{30 \text{ mi}} = \frac{9 \text{ cm}}{n \text{ mi}}$$

You do not have to include the dimensions in the proportion:

$$\frac{4}{30} = \frac{9}{n}$$

STEP 2: Solve the proportion by cross-multiplying.

$4 \times n = 9 \times 30 = 270$ or $4n = 270$

$n = 67.5$ miles

SOLUTION: **The approximate distance from Baltimore to Hagerstown is 68 miles.**

Rates

A rate is a fixed ratio between two quantities of different units, such as miles and hours, dollars and hours, points and games. If the second number of a rate is 1, then the rate is called a unit rate. 60 miles per hour and $15 per hour are unit rates.

Example 2

Last week Miguel worked 30 hours and earned $240. What was his rate of pay?

STRATEGY: **Divide the total earned by the number of hours.**

STEP 1:   How much money did Miguel earn?

He earned $240.

STEP 2:   How many hours did he work?

He worked 30 hours.

STEP 3:   Find the rate of pay.

Divide the amount of money earned by the number of hours worked.

$$\frac{\text{amount of money}}{\text{number of hours}} = \frac{240}{30} = \$8 \text{ per hour}$$

SOLUTION: **Miguel earned $8 per hour.**

The solution to Example 2 is a unit rate.

Example 3

The unit price of a can of tuna fish at the GHK Supermarket is $2.43. How much will 7 cans cost?

STRATEGY: **Use the definition of unit price.**

Unit price means the price of one unit, or the price of one can of tuna fish.

So, one can costs $2.43.

To find 7 cans, multiply: $7 \times 2.43 = \$17.01$

SOLUTION: **Seven cans of tuna fish cost $17.01.**

Sample Test Questions

1 A scale on a map reads:
2.5 inches = 50 miles. If you measure a distance on the map of 12.25 inches between two cities, how far is the actual distance between the cities?

A 215 miles

B 225 miles

C 235 miles

D 245 miles

2 Write as a unit price.

8 pounds of potatoes cost $3.60

A 35 cents

B 45 cents

C 55 cents

D 65 cents

3 In a recent survey, 3 out of 5 parents of the Heightstown School voted to extend the school year. If 240 parents voted, how many voted to extend the school year?

A 144

B 160

C 168

D 196

4 3 out of 25 high school students in Gilda's school say they do not like sports. If there are 425 students in her school, how many students do not like sports?

5 Harrieta typed 2,035 words in 37 minutes. What was her unit rate?

A 35 words per minute

B 45 words per minute

C 55 words per minute

D 65 words per minute

Go On ➡

Brief Constructed Response

6   Gordon bought a 14-oz box of Nutrition Plus cereal for $5.35, while Gladys bought a 12-oz box of Sweet and Delicious cereal for $4.22.

Step A   Compare unit prices of the cereals to find which one is less expensive.

_____

_____

Step B   Use what you know about unit prices to explain why your answer is correct. Use words and/or numbers in your explanation.

_____

_____

_____

_____

Progress Check for Lessons 17–20

1 The distance around a circular path surrounding a fountain in front of Jeb's school is 31.4 m. What is the radius of the circle to the nearest tenth of a meter? (Use $\pi = 3.14$)

A 98.6 m   C 5.2 m

B 10.0 m   D 5.0 m

2 Find the volume of this cylinder. (Use $\pi = 3.14$)

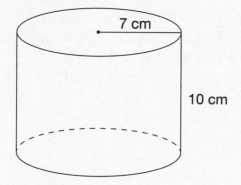

A 1538.6 cu cm

B 2198 cu cm

C 2738.2 cu cm

D 3077.2 cu cm

3 Which of the following would be the best approximation of the area of a circle with radius equal to 10?

A 3.14×10^2

B 3.14×10^3

C $3.14 \times 2 \times 10^2$

D $\frac{1}{2}(3.14 \times 10^2)$

4 The scale on the map on the wall of Georgia's classroom is 3 in = 400 mi. How many miles apart are two cities that measure 6.5 inches on the map? (Answer to the nearest whole number.)

5 Kal estimates that his son, who is 1.1 meters tall, is growing at the rate of 25 cm every 15 months. If this rate continues, how tall will his son be in two years?

A 1.3 m   C 1.5 m

B 1.4 m   D 1.6 m

6 Omar drew a circle and computed the area at 1256 sq cm. Find the radius of the circle. (Use $\pi = 3.14$)

A 400   C 20

B 40   D 10

Go On ➡

Standard 3.0: Measurement

Constructed Response Questions

Extended Constructed Response

7   This figure is called a composite figure.

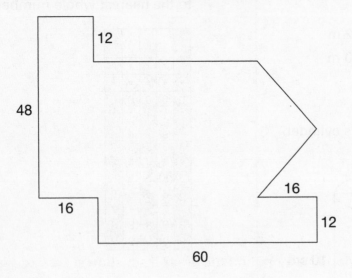

Step A   Find the area of this figure.

_____

Go On ➡

Step B • Use what you know about composite figures to explain why your answer is correct. Use words and/or diagrams in your explanation.

_____

_____

• Is there another way to find the area? If so, show a second way.

_____

_____

_____

_____

Statistics

In this unit you will learn about statistics. Statistics is the study of data. One way to display related data is to make a scatter plot.

Try This

You will need:

- a partner
- grid paper
- a ruler

Follow these steps:

1. Copy this coordinate grid on a piece of grid paper.

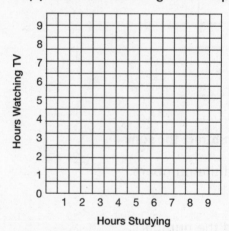

2. With your partner, graph these data as ordered pairs (studying, watching TV) on your grid.

Hours Studying	1	3	2	8	4	3	7	5	7	5
Hours Watching TV	8	6	7	2	6	8	3	4	1	5

3. In your own words describe any patterns you and your partner see in how the points are "scattered" in your scatter plot.

Think about it:

What conclusion could a person make from looking at the data in your scatter plot?

If you gathered data from 10 of your classmates, do you think the scatter plot of the data would look the same as the one you just made? Explain.

Standard 4.B.1.a

LESSON 21 Interpreting Tables

A table contains numerical information or data.

Example

How many more computers are in Room 108 than in Room 215?

Computers in Computer Labs at Blake Middle School

Classroom	PC	Macintosh
104	18	8
108	12	6
207	5	11
215	8	7
302	4	9

STRATEGY: **Add the numbers in the two different rows and subtract the sums.**

STEP 1: Find the row for Room 108 and add the numbers.

$12 + 6 = 18$

STEP 2: Find the row for Room 215 and add the numbers.

$8 + 7 = 15$

STEP 3: Subtract the sum for Room 215 from the sum for Room 108.

$18 - 15 = 3$

SOLUTION: **There are 3 more computers in Room 108.**

Sample Test Questions

Use this table for Questions 1–4.

Distance (in kilometers) Between Cities

	Foster	Grayson
Amesville	2.5	4.8
Bay City	8.3	6.4
Clayton	10.2	12.5
Duanne City	15	17
Easton	9.1	1.5

1 How much farther is Clayton from Grayson than from Foster?

A 22.7 km

B 5.5 km

C 2.3 km

D 1.9 km

2 How much farther is Easton from Foster than Bay City is from Foster?

A 0.8 km

B 1.8 km

C 8.4 km

D 17.4 km

3 Suppose you traveled from Amesville to Grayson and then from Grayson to Duanne City. How many kilometers would you travel?

A 4.8 km

B 12.2 km

C 17.3 km

D 21.8 km

4 Suppose you travel from Bay City to Foster, then from Foster to Easton. How many kilometers would you travel?

Go On ➡

129

Brief Constructed Response

5

	Departs from Baltimore	Arrives in New York City
Bus A	10:00 A.M.	3:00 P.M.
Bus B	11:00 A.M.	4:00 P.M.
Bus C	11:30 A.M.	4:30 P.M.
Bus D	12:00 Noon	4:00 P.M.

Step A   How much longer is the ride on Bus A than on Bus D?

_____

Step B   Use what you know about interpreting data in tables to explain why your answer is correct. Use words and/or numbers to support your explanation.

_____

_____

_____

_____

Standards 4.A.1.a, d

LESSON 22 Circle Graphs

A circle graph is useful when you want to compare parts of a whole.

Example 1

This circle graph shows the favorite pastimes of a group of eighth graders.

Favorite Pastimes

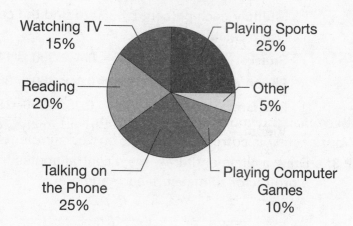

1   Which two activities were equally popular?

2   What percent of students chose Reading or Watching TV?

STRATEGY: Use the data in the circle graph.

1   Look for activities with the same percent.
Playing Sports and Talking on the Phone are each 25%.

SOLUTION: **Playing Sports and Talking on the Phone were equally popular.**

2   Find the sum of the percents for Reading and Watching TV.
20% + 15% = 35%

SOLUTION: **35% of the students chose Reading or Watching TV.**

Example 2

Lynisa received a $40 allowance last month. She estimated that she spent $16 on snacks, $4 on phone calls, $10 on bus fare to the mall, and $10 on a video. Create a circle graph to display and compare her expenses for the month.

STRATEGY: **Construct the graph by using percents.**

STEP 1: Compute the percent of the whole for each expense.

The whole is the $40 Lynisa started with. These are the computations of the percents for all expenses:

Snacks: $\frac{16}{40} = \frac{2}{5} = 40\%$ **Bus fare:** $\frac{10}{40} = \frac{1}{4} = 25\%$

Phone calls: $\frac{4}{40} = \frac{1}{10} = 10\%$ **Video:** $\frac{10}{40} = \frac{1}{4} = 25\%$

STEP 2: Find the measure of the central angle representing each percent.

There are 360° around a circle.

Multiply each percent by 360 to find the central angle. Use a calculator.

Snacks: 40% of 360° = 0.4 × 360 = 144°

Phone calls: 10% of 360° = 0.1 × 360 = 36°

Bus fare: 25% of 360° = 0.25 × 360 = 90°

Video: 25% of 360° = 0.25 × 260 = 90°

STEP 3: Draw a circle and draw the 4 central angles from Step 2. Use a protractor to measure each angle.

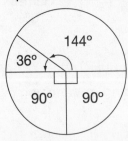

STEP 4: Label each section of the graph.

SOLUTION: **This circle graph compares Lynisa's expenses last month.**

Lynisa's Expenses Last Month

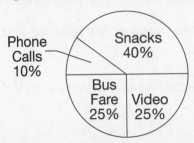

Sample Test Questions

For Questions 1–4, use this circle graph. It compares the ways students get to school.

How Students Go to School

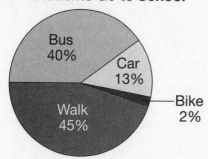

1 What percent of the students get to school by bus?

A 13%

B 40%

C 45%

D 80%

2 What is the measure of the central angle that represents students who walk to school?

A 150°

B 162°

C 170°

D 182°

3 What percent of students go to school by car or walk?

A 13%

B 32%

C 45%

D 58%

4 Which two categories make up about $\frac{1}{6}$ of the students?

A Bus and Car

B Bus and Bike

C Car and Bike

D Walk and Bike

Go On ➡

Extended Constructed Response

5   Here are the results of a survey to learn about favorite sandwiches served in a school cafeteria.

Favorite Cafeteria Sandwiches

Tuna	40%
Cheese	30%
Burger	20%
Egg Salad	10%

Step A   How many degrees would each sandwich have in a circle graph?

_____

_____

_____

_____

Go On ➡

Step B • Use what you know about translating percents into degree measures of a circle to explain why your answer is correct.

_____

_____

_____

_____

• Use your answer in Step A to make a circle graph using the given circle below. Make sure to label your graph. Explain why your graph is correct.

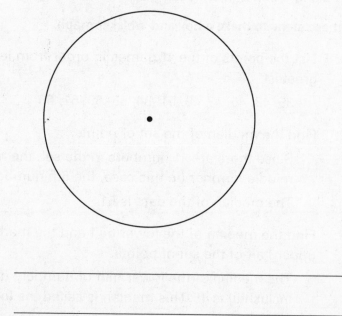

_____

_____

135

LESSON

23 Box-and-Whisker Plots

A box-and-whisker plot (or graph) shows how much a set of data is bunched together or spread out.

Example

The coach of the Pirates basketball team was analyzing the results of the first 11 games of the season. One set of data he looked at was the number of points his team scored in each game:

45 61 51 55 66 59

49 47 43 35 54

Analyze the data by making a box-and-whisker graph.

STRATEGY: **Follow these steps to make a box-and-whisker graph.**

STEP 1: List the points of the 11 games in order from least to greatest:

35, 43, 45, 47, 49, 51, 54, 55, 59, 61, 66

STEP 2: Find the median of the set of points.

Since there are 11 numbers in the set, the median is the middle number (in this case, the 6th number).

The median of the data is 51.

STEP 3: Find the median of the lower half and the median of the upper half of the set of points.

The median of the lower half of numbers (from 35 to 49, inclusive) is 45. This median is called the **lower quartile**.

The median of the upper half of numbers (from 54 to 66, inclusive) is 59. This median is called the **upper quartile**.

STEP 4: Now you have enough data to draw the graph.

a. Start by drawing a number line.

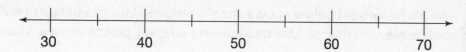

b. Above the number line, draw a box extending from the lower quartile (45) to the upper quartile (59). Draw in the median (51) as a dotted line.

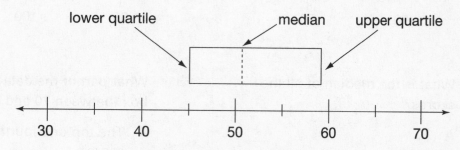

c. Draw two whiskers from the box. One extends to the lowest number of your data (35). The other goes to the highest number of your data (66). These two numbers are called the **lower extreme** and the **upper extreme**. Place a dot at each extreme.

SOLUTION: **Here is the completed graph, with all parts labeled.**

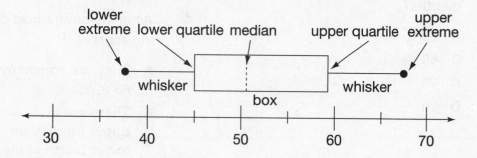

137

Sample Test Questions

The box-and-whisker plot below shows the scores one class of students received on a recent math achievement test. Use this box-and-whisker plot to answer Questions 1–4.

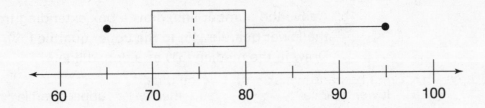

1 What is the median of all the scores?

    A 70

    B 74

    C 80

    D 95

2 What number is the lower quartile?

    A 85

    B 80

    C 75

    D 70

3 What part of the data is in the box (between 70 and 80)?

    A The top one-fourth of the scores.

    B The middle half of the scores.

    C The lower half of the scores.

    D The lower fourth of the scores.

4 What statement best describes the scores?

    A They are spread evenly from 65 to 95.

    B There are more scores in the upper fourth than in the lower fourth of the scores.

    C The scores are bunched closer together in the lowest fourth of the scores than in the highest fourth.

    D The mean of the scores is 74.

Go On ➡

Extended Constructed Response

5 These data represent the amounts of money in dollars raised by 11 students who participated in a charity walk.

40   48   50   52   54

56   59   60   64   66   71

Step A   Make a box-and-whisker plot of the data.

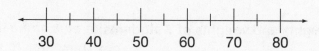

Step B   • Use what you know about making box-and-whisker plots to explain why your answer is correct. Use words and/or numbers to support your explanation.

_____

_____

_____

• Write a question that could be answered by a person reading your box-and-whisker plot.

_____

_____

_____

LESSON 24 Scatter Diagrams

A scatter diagram (also called a scatter plot) is a graph that contains many data points. Its purpose is to show relationships between two sets of data, like height and weight.

Example

This table shows the heights and weights of 7 students.

Height (in.)	40	45	50	53	50	60	55
Weight (lb)	50	70	80	100	110	140	150

Draw a scatter diagram for these data and determine the relationship between height and weight.

STRATEGY: **Be careful when you place the data points on the graph.**

STEP 1: Draw and label the scales for the graph. (In most cases, it does not matter which set of data is shown on the vertical axis or the horizontal axis.)

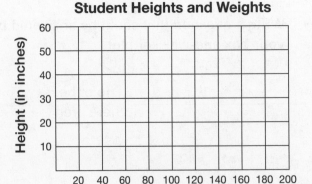

Student Heights and Weights

STEP 2: Draw dots for the data points.

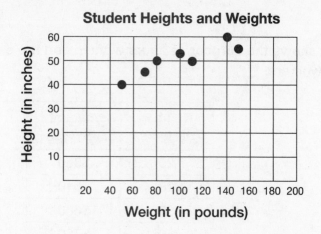

STEP 3: Draw a line that shows the general trend of the data points.

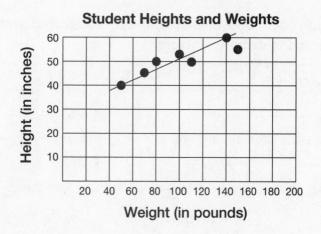

STEP 4: Study the points and the line to see if there is a relationship between height and weight.

Notice that as the height becomes greater, so does the weight.

SOLUTION: **As height increases, so does weight.**

The line drawn in the example is called the **line of best fit**. This line shows the trend in a scatter diagram. Sometimes, however, there aren't any trends.

Sample Test Questions

1 This chart shows the number of hours worked and the earnings of 5 factory workers.

Number of Hours	Amount Earned (dollars)
20	$350
28	$510
38	$660
40	$720
42	$800

Which graph could be a display of the hours worked and the amount of money earned by factory workers?

A

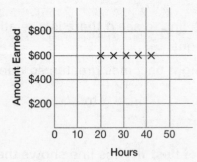

C

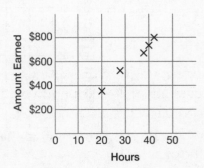

B

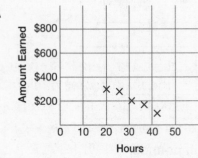

D

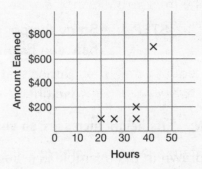

Go On ➡

2 Suppose you had a chart showing the income of 10 families and the last four digits of their phone numbers. Which of these is the most probable scatter diagram?

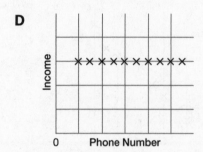

3 Suppose you had these two sets of data about 10 cities north of the equator: the distances from the equator and the temperatures in those cities on January 1. What is the most probable relationship between these two sets of data?

A   As the distances from the equator increase, the temperatures increase.

B   As the distances from the equator increase, the temperatures decrease.

C   There is no relationship between the two sets of data.

D   As the distances from the equator increase, the temperatures stay the same.

4 If you drew a scatter diagram of the math scores of eighth–grade students (vertical scale) and their heights, what type of line of best fit would you expect?

A   a line with positive slope

B   a line with negative slope

C   a horizontal line

D   It would not be possible to draw a trend line through the points.

Go On ➡

5 What would you expect to be the most likely scatter diagram for the relationship between these sets of data concerning cars: their size, and the distance they travel on a gallon of gasoline?

A

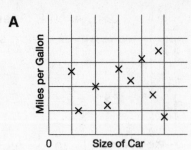

C

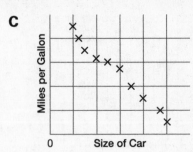

B

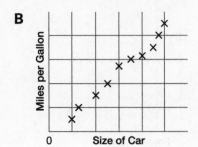

D

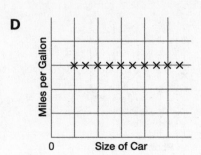

Extended Constructed Response

6 This table shows the noontime temperature in degrees Celsius on 8 different days throughout the year and the number of customers in an ice cream store.

Temperature (°C)	5°	10°	20°	15°	30°	25°	25°	17°
Customers	20	15	35	30	50	30	40	25

Step A Make a scatter plot for this data.

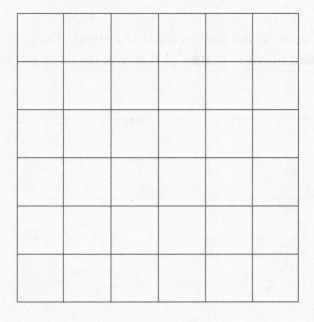

Go On ➡

Step B

• Use what you know about scatter plots to explain why your answer is correct. Use words and/or numbers to support your explanation.

_____

_____

_____

_____

• Use your scatter plot to identify a trend, if any, in the data. Explain how the scatter plot shows (or does not show) the trend.

_____

_____

_____

_____

Progress Check for Lessons 21–24

1 Ms. Rogers and Mr. Nelson sell cars at a used-car lot. This chart shows the number of cars they sold over a five-month period.

Number of Cars Sold

	Ms. Rogers	Mr. Nelson
January	5	3
February	1	2
March	7	9
April	12	15
May	18	14

How many more cars did they sell in April than in February?

Use this circle graph showing the results of a survey of 500 eighth graders for Question 2.

Favorite Sports

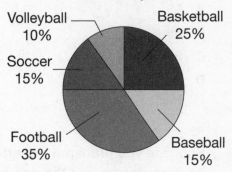

2 Which two sports were named as favorites by more than half the students surveyed?

A   soccer and volleyball

B   football and soccer

C   football and baseball

D   football and basketball

Go On ➡

3 This box-and-whisker plot shows the scores on a recent history exam.

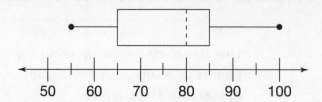

What number is the lower quartile?

A 55

B 65

C 80

D 85

4 Suppose you prepared a chart of the numbers on the uniforms of players on a basketball team and the number of points each player scored. Which of these would be the most probable scatter plot of the data?

A
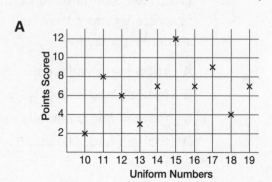

C
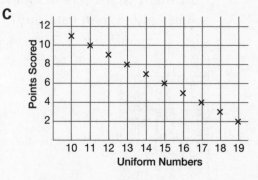

B
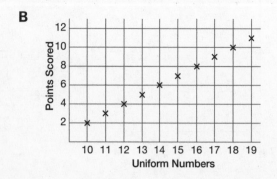

D
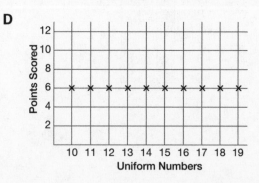

Go On ➡

148

Standard 4.0: Statistics

Constructed Response Questions

Brief Constructed Response

5 These box-and-whisker plots show the distribution of algebra test scores for two classes.

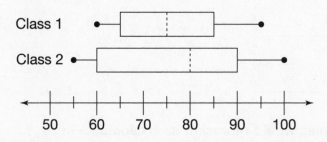

Step A What is the value of the *lowest* median score for the two classes?

_____

Step B Use what you know about box-and-whisker plots to explain why your answer is correct. Use words and/or numbers to support your explanation.

_____

_____

_____

_____

_____

Go On ➡

Extended Constructed Response

6 This data shows the percent of the vote received by candidates in a school election.

Election Results

Candidate	Percentage of Vote
Johnson	10
Kelada	15
Lester	50
Moore	25

Step A How many degrees would represent each candidate in a circle graph?

_____

_____

_____

_____

Step B • Use what you know about translating percents into degree measures of a circle to explain why your answer is correct. Use words and/or numbers to support your explanation.

_____

_____

_____

_____

• Use your answer in Step A to make a circle graph using the given circle below. Make sure you label your graph. Write a question that could be answered by a person reading your circle graph.

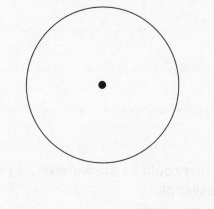

_____

_____

_____

Go On ➡

7 This data represents the ages of volunteer tutors in a community learn-to-read program.

42   50   52   54   56

58   61   62   66   68   73

Step A   Make a box-and-whisker plot of the data.

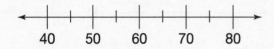

Step B   • Use what you know about making box-and-whisker plots to explain why your answer is correct. Use words and/or numbers to support your explanation.

_____

_____

_____

_____

• Write a question that could be answered by a person reading your box-and-whisker plot.

_____

_____

_____

Go On ➡

8 These data show the scores on an exam and the number of minutes spent studying for the exam.

Test Score	40	50	70	100	70	90	90	100
Minutes Studied	30	60	60	60	90	120	150	150

Step A Make a scatter plot for this data.

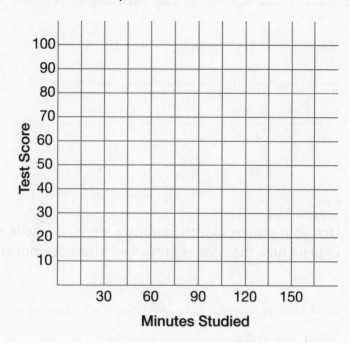

Step B

- Use what you know about making scatter plots to explain why your answer is correct. Use words and/or numbers to support your explanation.

_____

_____

_____

_____

- Use your scatter plot to identify a trend, if any, in the data. Explain how the scatter plot shows (or does not show) the trend.

_____

_____

_____

_____

Probability

In this unit you will learn about probability. Probability is the study of what is certain, likely, or impossible to happen.

Try This

You will need:

- a partner
- two number cubes
- paper and pencil

Follow these steps:

1. When you roll two number cubes, the possible sums of the numbers that come up are 2, 3, 4, 5, 6, 7, 8, 9, 10, 11, and 12.

2. With your partner, make a prediction of the sum that you think will come up most often and the sum that will come up least often. Write down your predictions.

3. Perform the experiment of rolling two number cubes and recording the sum. Have one partner roll the number cubes 50 times while the other records the results using tally marks (| = 1; ||||| = 5) in a chart like the one shown below. Then the partners switch roles and do the experiment 50 more times, making a total of 100 times.

Experiment: Rolling 2 number cubes

Sum	Tally
2	
3	
4	
5	
6	
7	
8	
9	
10	
11	
12	

4. Compare your results with your predictions. Were your predictions correct?

Think about it:

Can you think of why certain sums come up more often than others?
(Hint: Think of the possible addends for each sum in this experiment.)

LESSON 25

Outcomes of Independent Events

A number cube has 6 faces.

If you perform the experiment of tossing this number cube, there are 6 possible **outcomes**: 1, 2, 3, 4, 5, or 6.

This spinner has four equal sectors. If you perform the experiment of spinning this spinner, there are 4 possible outcomes: A, B, C, or D.

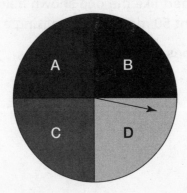

What if you performed the experiment of spinning the spinner and tossing the number cube?

Example 1

What is the total number of outcomes for spinning the spinner and tossing the number cube shown above?

STRATEGY: **Make a tree diagram.**

STEP 1:   List the outcomes for spinning the spinner and tossing the number cube.

A, or B, or C, or D   1, or 2, or 3, or 4, or 5, or 6

STEP 2:   Use the outcomes to make a tree diagram.

Think of the experiment as spinning the spinner and then tossing the number cube.

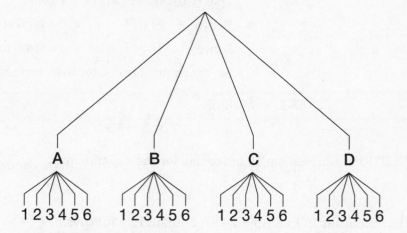

STEP 3:   Trace each path.

Start from the top of the diagram. Each path is an outcome:

A-1, A-2, A-3, A-4, A-5, A-6,

B-1, B-2, B-3, B-4, B-5, B-6,

C-1, C-2, C-3, C-4, C-5, C-6,

D-1, D-2, D-3, D-4, D-5, D-6

SOLUTION: **There are 24 outcomes for the experiment.**

Spinning a sector on a spinner and tossing a number with the number cube are independent events because the outcome of tossing the number cube and the outcome of spinning the spinner have no effect on one another. When events are independent, the number of outcomes equals the product of the number of outcomes in each event.

Example 2

What is the total number of outcomes for tossing a penny, a nickel, a dime, and a quarter?

STRATEGY: **Multiply the outcomes for each coin.**

STEP 1: List the outcome for tossing each coin.

Use H for heads and T for tails.

Penny	H or T	**Nickel**	H or T
Dime	H or T	**Quarter**	H or T

So there are two outcomes for each.

STEP 2: Multiply.

$2 \times 2 \times 2 \times 2 = 16$

SOLUTION: **There are 16 outcomes for the experiment.**

The outcomes in Example 2 can be listed as follows:

Outcomes with:

4 Heads	3 Heads	2 Heads	1 Head	No Heads
H-H-H-H	H-H-H-T	H-H-T-T	H-T-T-T	T-T-T-T
	H-H-T-H	H-T-H-T	T-H-T-T	
	H-T-H-H	H-T-T-H	T-T-H-T	
	T-H-H-H	T-H-T-H	T-T-T-H	
		T-T-H-H		
		T-H-H-T		

Sample Test Questions

For Questions 1–4, find the total number of outcomes for the given experiment.

1 Spinning this spinner and tossing this coin:

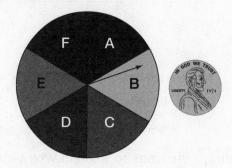

- A 6
- B 12
- C 24
- D 36

2 Rolling two number cubes with faces numbered 1 through 6 and tossing a dime.

- A 12
- B 24
- C 36
- D 72

3 Tossing a penny, rolling a number cube, and spinning this spinner:

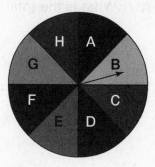

- A 64
- B 72
- C 96
- D 108

4 Tossing a dime, rolling a number cube, spinning a spinner with 5 equal sectors, and drawing a card from a deck of 6 cards labeled A, B, C, D, E, and F.

Go On ➡

Brief Constructed Response

5 Ciro designed an experiment consisting of rolling a number cube with faces numbered 1 through 6, tossing a nickel, tossing a dime, and tossing a quarter.

Step A What is the total number of outcomes for Ciro's experiment?

_____

Step B Use what you know about finding outcomes to explain why your answer is correct. Use words, numbers, and/or diagrams to support your explanation.

_____

_____

_____

_____

_____

Standard 5.B.1.a

LESSON 26
Probability of Independent Events

Probability is a way to measure the chance that an event will occur. You can use this ratio to find the probability, p, of an event:

$$p = \frac{\text{number of favorable outcomes}}{\text{number of possible outcomes}}$$

Two events are independent when the outcome of one event has no effect on the outcome of another event. For example,

Event: tossing a coin and getting tails

Event: tossing a number cube and getting a number less than 5

When finding the probability of two independent events, multiply the probabilities of the two events to get the total probability. This is called the multiplication rule.

Example 1

Find the probability of tossing a coin and getting tails and tossing a number cube and getting a number less than 5.

STRATEGY: **Find the probability of each event and apply the multiplication rule.**

STEP 1: Find the probability of each event.

Tossing the coin:

Probability of tails = $\frac{\text{number of favorable outcomes}}{\text{number of possible outcomes}} = \frac{1}{2}$

Tossing the number cube:

There are four favorable outcomes: 1, 2, 3, and 4.

Probability of a number $< 5 = \frac{\text{number of favorable outcomes}}{\text{number of possible outcomes}}$

$= \frac{4}{6} = \frac{2}{3}$

STEP 2: Apply the multiplication rule.

Probability of tails $\times$ Probability of a number $< 5 =$

$\frac{1}{2} \times \frac{2}{3} = \frac{2}{6} = \frac{1}{3}$

SOLUTION: **The probability is $\frac{1}{3}$.**

Probability ratios can also be expressed as decimals or percents.

Example 2

Jack heard the weather forecast on TV: the probability of rain today is 50% and the probability of rain tomorrow is 50%. What is the probability that it will rain on both days?

STRATEGY: **Use the multiplication rule.**

STEP 1: Change the probabilities to fractions.

$$50\% = 0.50 = \frac{50}{100} = \frac{1}{2}$$

$$50\% = 0.50 = \frac{50}{100} = \frac{1}{2}$$

STEP 2: Apply the multiplication rule.

$$\frac{1}{2} \times \frac{1}{2} = \frac{1}{4}$$

$$\frac{1}{4} = \frac{25}{100} = 25\%$$

SOLUTION: **The probability that it will rain on both days is 25%.**

NOTE: You could also have expressed the probability as 0.25 or $\frac{1}{4}$.

Sample Test Questions

1 What is the probability that a "4" will appear when you toss 2 six-sided dice?

A $\frac{1}{36}$

B $\frac{1}{12}$

C $\frac{1}{6}$

D $\frac{1}{3}$

2 Mike has 25 red tiles, 10 green tiles, and 15 blue tiles in a paper bag. If he chooses a tile at random, returns it to the bag, and then chooses a second tile, what is the probability that the two tiles will be green and blue in that order?

A 0.6

B 0.3

C 0.06

D 0.03

3 The weather forecast reports that the probability of rain today is 20% and the probability of rain tomorrow is 50%. What is the probability that it will rain on both days?

A 10%

B 30%

C 70%

D 100%

4 What is the probability of getting a number less than 3 in two tosses of a single die?

A $\frac{1}{2}$

B $\frac{1}{3}$

C $\frac{1}{6}$

D $\frac{1}{9}$

Go On ➡

Brief Constructed Response

5 Roland performed the experiment of tossing a number cube and spinning this spinner.

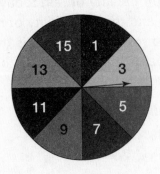

Step A What is the probability that Roland will toss a number less than 6 and spin a number greater than 6?

_____

Step B Use what you know about probability of independent events to explain why your answer is correct. Use words and/or numbers to support your explanation.

164

LESSON 27

Probability of Dependent Events

Two events are **dependent** when the outcome of one event is affected by the outcome of the other. The events in the following example are dependent.

Example

A bag contains 3 green, 3 blue, and 3 yellow marbles. What is the probability of drawing a blue marble followed by a yellow marble in that order when you draw two marbles from the bag without returning the first marble to the bag?

STRATEGY: **Use the multiplication rule.**

STEP 1: Find the probability of getting blue as the first marble.

3 of the 9 marbles are blue.

The probability of getting a blue marble is:

$$\frac{\text{number of favorable outcomes}}{\text{number of possible outcomes}} = \frac{3}{9} = \frac{1}{3}$$

STEP 2: Find the probability of getting yellow as the second marble.

After the first selection, 8 marbles remain in the bag. The number of possible outcomes has changed from 9 to 8, so this event is dependent on the first.

The probability of getting yellow is:

$$\frac{\text{number of favorable outcomes}}{\text{number of possible outcomes}} = \frac{3}{8}$$

STEP 3: Apply the multiplication rule.

$$\frac{1}{3} \times \frac{3}{8} = \frac{3}{24} = \frac{1}{8}$$

SOLUTION: **The probability of getting blue and then yellow without returning the first marble to the bag is $\frac{1}{8}$.**

Remember: You could also express the probability as a decimal or as a percent:

$$\frac{1}{8} = 1 \div 8 = 0.125 \qquad\qquad 0.125 = 12.5\%$$

Sample Test Questions

1 An envelope contains 5 cards numbered from 1 through 5. What is the probability of drawing the "2" card followed by the "3" card if you do not return the first card to the envelope?

A 0.05

B 0.15

C 0.20

D 0.50

2 Jim has 4 quarters, 3 dimes, and 3 nickels in his pocket. What is the probability that he will get a dime followed by a nickel when he pulls two coins out of his pocket?

A 9%

B 10%

C 20%

D 63%

3 The teacher wrote the names of each student on a card and placed the cards in a bag. There are 8 boys and 12 girls in the class. What is the probability that the teacher will draw the name of a girl followed by the name of a boy when she draws two cards from the bag?

A $\frac{6}{25}$

B $\frac{24}{95}$

C $\frac{2}{3}$

D $\frac{19}{25}$

4 A bag contains 4 red tiles, 3 blue tiles, 2 green tiles, and 1 yellow tile. What is the probability of drawing a blue tile and then another blue tile if the first tile is not returned to the bag?

A $\frac{3}{50}$

B $\frac{1}{15}$

C $\frac{1}{5}$

D $\frac{3}{10}$

Go On ➡

Brief Constructed Response

5 The school chess club has 6 girls and 4 boys. Two students are to be selected at random to represent their school in a statewide tournament. The coordinator of the club writes each student's name on a card and places the cards in a paper bag.

Step A What is the probability that the coordinator will draw the name of a girl followed by the name of a boy?

_____

Step B Use what you know about finding probability of dependent events to explain why your answer is correct. Use words and/or numbers to support your explanation.

_____

_____

_____

_____

STOP

LESSON

28 Experimental Probability

Surveys are used to gather information about a group. A part of the group is selected to represent the entire group. That part is called the **sample**. You use the information from a sample to make a prediction about the whole group.

A good method to use when selecting members of the group is random selection. Each member of the group has an equal chance of being selected.

Example 1

Gary took a survey of 30 students in three different grades to find out if they are in favor of going to school in the summer. Here are the results of his survey:

	7th Grade	8th Grade	9th Grade
Yes	12	10	14
No	10	14	14
Not Sure	8	6	2

Based on these results, what is a good estimate of the percent of students who are interested in going to school in the summer?

STRATEGY: Include all the students.

STEP 1: Find the total number of all "yes" votes.

Add: 12 + 10 + 14 = 36

STEP 2: Find the total number of students surveyed.

30 + 30 + 30 = 90

STEP 3: Find the percent of "yes" votes out of the total.

$\frac{36}{90} = \frac{x}{100}$

$x = 40$ or 40%

SOLUTION: **A good estimate of the percent of students who are in favor of going to school in the summer is 40%.**

If Gary's sample was random, his results (40%) mean that the probability that the whole school population of 7th, 8th, and 9th graders in favor of going to summer school is 40%.

Example 2

If the total number of 8th-grade students in Gary's school is 180, what would be a good prediction of the number of 8th graders who are not sure if they are in favor of going to summer school?

STRATEGY: **Multiply the total number of students by the probability.**

Find the probability.

Look at the column in the table for 8th Grade.

Probability $= \frac{6}{30} = \frac{1}{5}$

$\frac{1}{5}$ of $180 = \frac{180}{5} = 36$

SOLUTION: **A good prediction of the number of 8th-grade students who are not sure if they are in favor of summer school is 36.**

Example 3

In a random survey, 30 out of 50 adults in a certain town said that they approved of a curfew for students below the age of 16.

1 What is the probability that a person chosen from the sample surveyed approves of a curfew?

2 If there are 1500 adults in the town, predict the total number of people who would approve of a curfew.

STRATEGY: **Find the probability and use it to make a prediction.**

STEP 1: Find the probability.

$$P = \frac{\text{favorable outcomes}}{\text{total outcomes}} = \frac{30}{50} = \frac{3}{5}$$

STEP 2: Use the probability.

$\frac{3}{5}$ of the sample (50) were in favor of a curfew.

$\frac{3}{5}$ of the total (1500) should be in favor of a curfew.

$\frac{3}{5}$ of $1500 = \frac{3}{5} \times \frac{1500}{1} = 900$

SOLUTION: **A good prediction of the number of people who would favor a curfew is 900.**

Remember: Since a probability can also be expressed as a decimal, you could have solved the problem in Example 3 by multiplying 1500 by 0.6, the decimal equivalent of $\frac{3}{5}$.

169

Sample Test Questions

1 Maura surveyed 25 people at random in her town and learned that 16 of those people were in favor of building a new community swimming pool. What is the probability that everyone in the town would favor the new swimming pool?

A 0.16

B 0.32

C 0.64

D 0.8

2 Forty-two out of 50 students surveyed in Julie's school said that they planned to go to college. What is the probability that a person chosen at random from the 600 students in Julie's school plans to go to college?

A 32%

B 42%

C 52%

D 84%

3 In a certain town, 28 out of 80 adults surveyed at random said that they own a cellular phone. What is the probability that an adult chosen at random from the town owns a cellular phone?

A $\frac{13}{20}$

B $\frac{1}{3}$

C $\frac{7}{20}$

D $\frac{7}{40}$

4 Michael has a spinner that is divided into 8 equal parts. If he spins the spinner 72 times, how many times can he expect the arrow to land in the shaded area?

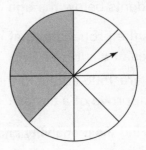

A 18

B 27

C 36

D 45

Go On ➡

5 Hillary is experimenting with a new way to shoot free throws. She took a sample of 80 free throws so that she could predict how well she would do over the entire season. She made 52. How many free throws out of 200 can she expect to make?

A 65

B 85

C 110

D 130

6 Doug asked a random sample of 50 of his schoolmates whether they were interested in extending the school year:

Yes	12
No	25
Not Sure	13

Based on this sample, how many students in his school favor extending the school year? Total enrollment: 250.

Go On ➡

Brief Constructed Response

7 In a school survey, 18 out of the 25 high school seniors chosen at random said that they plan to go to college.

Step A If there are 375 seniors in the school, what is a good prediction of the number of seniors who plan to go to college?

_____

Step B Use what you know about making predictions to explain why your prediction is a good one. Use words and/or numbers to support your explanation.

_____

_____

_____

_____

_____

STOP

Progress Check for Lessons 25–28

1 How many outcomes are there for tossing the following coins: a penny, a nickel, a dime, a quarter, and a half dollar?

A 10

B 32

C 64

D 128

2 What is the probability of tossing two number cubes and getting a number greater than 3 on one cube and a number less than 3 on the other?

A 0.16$\overline{6}$

B 0.40

C 0.50

D 0.75

3 A bag contains 4 red tiles, 3 blue tiles, 2 green tiles, and 1 yellow tile. What is the probability of drawing a green tile and then another green tile if the first tile is not returned to the bag?

A $\frac{1}{5}$

B $\frac{1}{9}$

C $\frac{1}{14}$

D $\frac{1}{45}$

4 Nilsa took a random survey of 40 students in three different grades to find out if they were in favor of the cafeteria changing its menu. Here are the results.

	7th Grade	8th Grade	9th Grade
Yes	19	15	19
No	19	17	15
Not Sure	2	8	6

What is the probability that an 8th grader chosen at random will not be sure if the cafeteria should change its menu?

A 5%   C 15%

B 10%   D 20%

5 Smith has a spinner that is divided into 7 equal parts. If he spins the spinner 77 times, how many times can he expect the arrow to land in the shaded region?

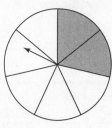

Go On ➡

Standard 5.0: Probability

Constructed Response Questions

Brief Constructed Response

6 The probability that there will be weekend homework in Shawn's math class is 30% and the probability that there will be weekend science homework is 50%.

Step A What is the probability that he will have both math and science homework next weekend?

_____

Step B Use what you know about probability of independent events to explain why your answer is correct. Use words and/or numbers to support your explanation.

_____

_____

_____

_____

Go On ➡

7 Marcia is a contestant on a quiz show. If she can draw 2 silver marbles from a box containing a total of 10 marbles, she wins a prize.

Step A What is the probability that she draws a silver marble and then another silver marble without replacing the first marble she draws?

_____

Step B Use what you know about probability of dependent events to explain why your answer is correct. Use words and/or numbers to support your explanation.

_____

_____

_____

_____

Extended Constructed Response

8 If you guess on a multiple-choice test that has 4 answer choices for each question, the probability of getting a correct answer is $\frac{1}{4}$.

Step A Suppose you guess on three consecutive questions. What is the probability that you will get all three correct?

_____

Step B • Use what you know about probability to explain why your answer is correct. Use words and/or numbers to support your explanation.

_____

_____

_____

• What is the probability that you will get all three wrong? Explain how you got your answer.

_____

_____

_____

_____

STOP

Number Relationships and Computation

In this unit you will learn about using numbers. You can use counters to learn about operations with numbers known as integers.

Try This

You will need:

- a partner
- pencil and paper for recording results
- a collection of yellow and red counters or small squares of paper labeled (+) or (−)

Follow these steps:

1. You can use counters to show subtraction of integers. For example, to find the difference 5 − 7, you start with 5 yellow (or positive) counters:

You need to take away 7 positive counters, so add 2 positive and 2 negative counters to the 5 counters. Adding the two positive and two negative counters is like adding zero, so the total value of the counters is still 5.

Now you can take away 7 positive counters, leaving 2 negative counters.

So, 5 − 7 = −2

2. You and your partner each take a small handful of positive counters. While your partner watches, arrange counters to find the lesser number minus the greater number. Have your partner record the result. For example, if you had 17 positive counters and 13 positive counters, your partner would record 13 − 17 = −4.

3. Switch roles until each of you has found at least two differences using the counters.

Think about it:

What shortcut could you use to find the sum of integers without using counters?

How could you use counters to show subtraction of a negative number, such as 7 − (−5)? How many pairs of positive and negative counters would you have to add so that you can take away 5 negative counters?

LESSON 29 Scientific Notation

Scientific notation is a special way of writing numbers. It is used in many different fields of science to show both very large and very small numbers.

Here are 3 numbers and their equivalents in scientific notation:

$$230,000 = 2.3 \times 10^5$$
$$0.00000105 = 1.05 \times 10^{-6}$$
$$4,761,000,000 = 4.761 \times 10^9$$

A number in scientific notation has two factors:

- The first factor is a number greater than or equal to 1 and less than 10.
- The second factor is a power of 10 (10 with an exponent). The exponent can be either positive or negative. A positive exponent indicates the number of times 10 is used as a factor, and a negative exponent indicates the number of times 10 is used as a divisor. Large numbers get positive exponents; very small numbers get negative exponents.

Example 1

Saturn is about 875,000,000 miles from the sun. How would this distance be represented in scientific notation?

STRATEGY: Write the number, using the two factors for scientific notation.

STEP 1: Write the first factor by using the three non-zero digits (875) of 875,000,000. Place a decimal point after the first digit:

The first factor becomes 8.75. Remember, this factor is a number greater than or equal to 1 but less than 10.

STEP 2: What number times 8.75 equals 875,000,000?

The number is 100,000,000 or 10^8, so 10^8 is the second factor.

Here's a quick way to find the exponent of 10: Count the number of decimal places after the first digit in 875,000,000.

There are 8 decimal places. So the exponent of 10 is 8: 10^8.

STEP 3: Write the two factors together.

$$875,000,000 = 8.75 \times 10^8$$

SOLUTION: **The distance of Saturn from the sun is 8.75×10^8 miles.**

> **NOTE:**
> The exponent 8 in the answer represents 8 places to the left from the original decimal point in 875,000,000.
>
> 8.75,000,000. *count 8 places to the left*

This analysis leads to these rules for finding the exponent for the second factor:

Rules for Finding the Exponent for the Second Factor

Count the number of places from the original decimal point to the decimal point of the first factor.

1 If you count to the **left** from the original decimal point, the exponent is **positive**. (The original number is **greater than 1**.)

2 If you count to the **right** from the original decimal point, the exponent is **negative**. (The original number is **less than 1**.)

Example 2

Write 0.00017 in scientific notation.

STRATEGY: **Use the Rules to find the exponent.**

STEP 1: Use the two non-zero digits of 0.00017 to write the first factor.

The two non-zero digits are 1 and 7.

The first factor is a number greater than or equal to 1 and less than 10.

In this case, 1.7 is the first factor.

STEP 2: Use the Rule to find the power of 10 for the second factor.

.0001.7 *count 4 places to the right*

The power of 10 is –4. (Part 2 of the Rules states that if you count to the right, the exponent is negative.)

STEP 3: Write the two factors together.

SOLUTION: **The number 0.00017 in scientific notation is 1.7×10^{-4}.**

Example 3

The height of a building is about 5,300 feet. Express this height in scientific notation.

STRATEGY: **Use the Rules to find the exponent.**

STEP 1: Write the first factor as a number between 1 and 10.

The first factor becomes 5.3.

STEP 2: Determine the factor of 10.

You count three places to the left from the original decimal point, so the exponent is positive 3.

SOLUTION: $5,300 = 5.3 \times 10^3$

Sample Test Questions

1 How would 4,500,000 be expressed in scientific notation?

A 4.5×10^6

B 4.5×10^7

C 4.5×10^5

D 450×10^4

2 How would 0.0000326 be expressed in scientific notation?

A 3.26×10^5

B 3.26×10^{-5}

C 3.26×10^{-4}

D 3.26×10^4

3 $5.624 \times 10^{-4} = ?$

A 0.005624

B 0.0005624

C 5624

D 56,240

4 $500,000 \times 6,000 = ?$

A 3×10^6

B 3×10^7

C 3×10^8

D 3×10^9

5 $3.28 \times 10^{-2} = ?$

A 328

B 0.328

C 0.0328

D 0.00328

6 A microsecond is equal to 10^{-6} seconds. How many seconds (in decimal form) is 7 microseconds?

A 7,000,000

B 0.7000006

C 0.000007

D 0.0000007

7 The planet Mars is 710,000,000 miles from the sun. What is this distance expressed in scientific notation?

A 7.1×10^8 miles

B 7.1×10^7 miles

C 7.1×10^6 miles

D 7.1×10^{-7} miles

8 A micron is a unit of measurement equivalent to 0.000039 inch. What is this distance expressed in scientific notation?

A 0.39×10^{-4} in.

B 3.9×10^{-4} in.

C 3.9×10^{-5} in.

D 3.9×10^{-6} in.

Go On ➡

Brief Constructed Response

9   When the planet Jupiter is closest to Earth, it is 366,000,000 miles from Earth.

Step A   Express this distance in scientific notation.

_____

_____

Step B   Use what you know about scientific notation to explain why your answer is correct. Use words and/or numbers to support your explanation.

_____

_____

_____

_____

182

LESSON 30

Comparing and Ordering Rational Numbers

Rational numbers are numbers that can be expressed as fractions that can be formed from integers. For example, $\frac{6}{7}$, $-\frac{3}{13}$, $-\frac{3}{4}$ are all rational numbers. Rational numbers include all decimals with a finite number of digits (0.5, 1.3652, and 4.0007) or repeating patterns (0.143143143...and $3.\overline{67}$).

One of the best ways to compare rational numbers is to write them as decimals.

Example 1

Which rational number is greater, $\frac{2}{3}$ or 0.676767...?

STRATEGY: **Write the fraction as a decimal and compare the numbers as decimals.**

STEP 1: Find the decimal equivalent of $\frac{2}{3}$.

If you do not know the decimal equivalent for $\frac{2}{3}$, then use your calculator.

 0.6666666

In your calculator window, this decimal will end after 7 or more digits, but the decimal is an infinite decimal of 6's. (Sometimes, you will see a 7 at the end of the 6's, if your calculator rounds off the last place it shows.)

$\frac{2}{3}$ = 0.6666666...

STEP 2: Compare the two decimals.

0.676767... > 0.6666666..., since the digit (7) in the hundredths place of 0.676767... is greater than the digit (6) in the hundredths place of 0.6666666...

SOLUTION: **0.676767... > $\frac{2}{3}$**

Remember that integers are also rational numbers because they can be expressed as the ratio of two integers. For example:

$2 = \frac{2}{1}$ $0 = \frac{0}{1}$ $-3 = -\frac{3}{1}$ or $\frac{3}{-1}$

The absolute value of a number is its distance from 0 on a number line. Since absolute value is a distance, it is always positive. For example,

$$|4| = 4 \qquad |{-4}| = 4$$

Example 2

Which number is greater, -80 or $|{-2}|$?

STRATEGY: Simplify the absolute value. Then compare.

STEP 1: Find $|{-2}|$.

$$|{-2}| = 2$$

STEP 2: Compare the numbers by imagining their positions on a number line.

On a number line, 2 would be to the right of -80, so 2 is greater.

SOLUTION: $|{-2}| > -80$, or $-80 < |{-2}|$

Example 3

Place these numbers in order from least to greatest: $5\frac{1}{6}$, 5.16, and $5.\overline{16}$.

STRATEGY: Compare the numbers as decimals.

STEP 1: Use your calculator to write $5\frac{1}{6}$ as a decimal.

STEP 2: Write out 6 places of $5.\overline{16}$

The symbol $\overline{16}$ means that the digits 1 and 6 keep repeating. Therefore, $5.\overline{16}$ is a repeating decimal.

$$5.\overline{16} = 5.161616\ldots$$

STEP 3: Compare the three numbers.

The three numbers all have the same whole number (5), the same number in the tenths place (1), and the same number in the hundredths place (6).

The number 5.16 can be written as 5.160. Its thousandths place contains a 0.

Comparing the digits in the thousandths places of the three numbers shows that 5.16 is the smallest, 5.161616... is the middle number, and 5.16666... is the largest.

SOLUTION: The order of the numbers from smallest to largest is 5.16, $5.\overline{16}$, and $5\frac{1}{6}$.

Sample Test Questions

1 Which is smaller, 0.66 or $\frac{2}{3}$, and why?

A $\frac{2}{3}$ is smaller because it has a smaller number in the hundredths place than 0.66.

B 0.66 is smaller because it has a smaller number in the hundredths place than $\frac{2}{3}$.

C $\frac{2}{3}$ is smaller because it has a smaller digit in the thousandths place than 0.66.

D 0.66 is smaller because it has a smaller digit in the thousandths place than $\frac{2}{3}$.

2 Which is greater, $\frac{3}{8}$ or 0.373737, and why?

A $\frac{3}{8}$ is greater because it has a greater digit in its thousandths place than 0.373737.

B 0.373737 is greater because it has a greater digit in its hundredths place than $\frac{3}{8}$.

C $\frac{3}{8}$ is greater because it has a greater digit in its hundredths place than 0.373737.

D 0.373737 is greater because it has a greater digit in its thousandths place than $\frac{3}{8}$.

3 Choose the least of these numbers.

A $\frac{3}{4}$ **C** $\frac{8}{11}$

B $\frac{5}{7}$ **D** 0.747474...

4 Place these numbers in order from least to greatest:

$\frac{3}{7}$, $\frac{2}{5}$, **and 0.4222**

A $\frac{2}{5}$, $\frac{3}{7}$, and 0.4222

B $\frac{3}{7}$, $\frac{2}{5}$, and 0.4222

C $\frac{2}{5}$, 0.4222, and $\frac{3}{7}$

D 0.4222, $\frac{2}{5}$, and $\frac{3}{7}$

5 Place these numbers in order from least to greatest:

0.$\overline{12}$, 0.12, and $\frac{1}{8}$

A $\frac{1}{8}$, 0.12, and 0.$\overline{12}$

B 0.$\overline{12}$, $\frac{1}{8}$, and 0.12

C 0.12, $\frac{1}{8}$, and 0.$\overline{12}$

D 0.12, 0.$\overline{12}$, and $\frac{1}{8}$

6 Choose the greatest of these numbers.

A 0.$\overline{12}$ **C** $\frac{1}{9}$

B 0.1   **D** 0.12

7 Which of the following lists the numbers from greatest to least?

A 5, –6, 0, $|-1|$

B –6, 5, 0, $|-1|$

C 5, 0, $|-1|$, –6

D 5, $|-1|$, 0, –6

8 Which of the following sentences is false?

A $|-1| > 0$ **C** $|-8| > |-9|$

B $0 > -9$ **D** $0 < |2|$

Brief Constructed Response

9 Three students got these answers to the same math problem:

$\frac{3}{8}$ 0.37   0.3

Step A Which is the least number?

_____

Step B Use what you know about comparing and ordering rational numbers to explain why your answer is correct. Use words and/or numbers to support your explanation.

_____

_____

_____

_____

Standard 6.C.1.a

LESSON 31

Addition, Subtraction, Multiplication, and Division of Integers

Learn the rules for the four basic operations with integers.

Rules for Adding Integers

1 Add the positive integers.

2 Add the negative integers without the signs.

3 Subtract the sum of the negative integers from the sum of the positive integers.

Example 1

$6 + (-14) + (-10) + 30 = ?$

STRATEGY: Follow the rules for adding integers.

STEP 1: Add the positive integers.

$6 + 30 = 36$

STEP 2: Add the negative integers without the signs.

$(-14) + (-10)$ becomes $14 + 10 = 24$

STEP 3: Subtract the sum of the negative numbers from the sum of the positive numbers.

$36 - 24 = 12$

SOLUTION: The answer is 12.

Rules for Subtracting Integers

To subtract one integer from another:

1 Change the sign of the number to be subtracted ("the second number"). If the second number is positive, make it negative; if the number is negative, make it positive.

2 Add the first number to the changed second number.

In other words, to subtract, add the opposite of the number.

Example 2

Subtract $16 - (-13) = ?$

STRATEGY: Follow the rules for subtracting integers.

STEP 1: Change the sign of the number to be subtracted (the second number).

(-13) becomes 13.

STEP 2: Add the first number to the changed second number.

$16 + 13 = 29$

SOLUTION: The answer is 29.

Rules for Multiplying Integers

1 Change any negative integers to positive integers.

2 Multiply the integers as positive numbers.

3 Find the sign of the product of two numbers by these rules:

    RULE 1: If the signs of the numbers are the same, then the product is **positive**.

    RULE 2: If the signs of the numbers are different, then the product is **negative**.

Example 3

Multiply: $(-25) \times (-8) \times (-2) = ?$

STRATEGY: **Follow the rules for multiplying integers.**

        STEP 1:   Change negative integers to positive integers.

                (-25), (-8), and (-2), become 25, 8, and 2.

        STEP 2:   Multiply the integers as positive numbers.

                $(25 \times 8) \times 2 = (200) \times 2 = 400$

        STEP 3:   Use the rules for finding the sign of the product.

                The product of the three negative numbers can be shown as follows:

                $(-) \times (-) \times (-)$

                The product of the first two negative numbers is positive (Rule 1):

                So, $(-) \times (-) \times (-) = (+) \times (-)$

                A positive number times a negative number equals a negative number (different signs, Rule 2).

                So, $(+) \times (-) = (-)$

                The sign of the product of the three negative numbers is negative.

SOLUTION: **The answer is −400.**

Rules for Dividing Integers

1 Change any negative integers to positive integers.

2 Divide the integers as positive numbers.

3 Find the sign of the quotient (the answer) by these rules:

RULE 1: If the signs of the numbers are the same, then the quotient is **positive**.

RULE 2: If the signs of the numbers are different, then the quotient is **negative**.

NOTE: The Rules for dividing integers are similar to the Rules for multiplying integers.

Example 4

Divide: $(-20) \div (5) = ?$

STRATEGY: Follow the rules for dividing integers.

STEP 1: Change negative integers to positive integers.

(-20) becomes 20.

STEP 2: Divide the integers as positive numbers.

$20 \div 5 = 4$

STEP 3: Use the rules for finding the sign of the quotient.

The quotient of a negative number divided by a positive number is a negative number (Rule 2):

In abbreviated form: $(-) \div (+) = (-)$

SOLUTION: The quotient is **−4**.

Sample Test Questions

1 $6 + 10 = ?$

A 16

B −16

C 4

D −4

2 $(-30) - (-120) = ?$

A 90

B −90

C 150

D −150

3 $4 \times (-8) = ?$

A 4

B 12

C −12

D −32

4 $(-60) \div (-4) = ?$

A 15

B −15

C 64

D −64

5 $(-2) \times (-3) \times (-5) = ?$

A 30

B −30

C 11

D −11

6 $(-5) \times (-7) \times (2) = ?$

A 14

B −14

C 70

D −70

7 $44 - (-12) = ?$

A 56

B −56

C 32

D −32

8 $(-300) - (-500) = ?$

A 200

B −200

C 800

D −800

9 $(-16) + (-19) = ?$

A 35

B −35

C 3

D −3

10 $(-40) + 17 = ?$

A 57

B −57

C 23

D −23

Go On ➡

Brief Constructed Response

11   In Melba's town the temperature at 6:00 A.M. was −8°F. By 2:00 P.M. the temperature had risen 22°.

Step A   What was the temperature in Melba's town at 2:00 P.M.?

_____

Step B   Use what you know about operations with integers to explain why your answer is correct. Use words and/or numbers to support your explanation.

_____

_____

_____

_____

_____

STOP

Standards 6.C.1.b, 6.C.2.a

LESSON 32 Square Roots

This lesson is about taking the square root—the opposite of squaring numbers. You square a number when you multiply the number by itself. To square 3, multiply $3 \times 3 = 9$, or $3^2 = 9$. We say, "3 squared is 9." Square numbers get their name from the square figure.

The area of this square is 3×3, or 3^2, or 3 squared. The opposite, or inverse, of squaring a number is taking the square root. The square root of 9 is 3, since $3^2 = 9$. The symbol for square root is $\sqrt{}$. We write $\sqrt{9} = 3$.

Example 1

Find $\sqrt{36}$.

STRATEGY: Think of a number which, when squared, equals 36.

$6^2 = 36$

SOLUTION: $\sqrt{36} = 6$

When the number under the square root symbol is not a square number, you can estimate the square root.

Example 2

Which integer is closest to $\sqrt{60}$?

STRATEGY: Think: between which two square numbers is 60?

60 is not the square of a whole number.
However, 60 is between the square numbers 49 and 64.
So, $\sqrt{60}$ is between $\sqrt{49}$ and $\sqrt{64}$.
Since $\sqrt{49} = 7$ and $\sqrt{64} = 8$, 60 is between 7 and 8.

SOLUTION: Since 60 is closer to 64 than to 49, $\sqrt{60}$ is closer to 8 than to 7.

Sample Test Questions

1 Find $\sqrt{25}$.

A 5

B 12.5

C 50

D 625

2 Find $\sqrt{100}$.

A 50

B 25

C 10

D 1

3 Find $\sqrt{16}$.

A 4

B 8

C 32

D 256

4 Find $\sqrt{81}$.

A 81

B 40.5

C 18

D 9

5 $\sqrt{40}$ is between which two whole numbers?

A 5 and 6

B 6 and 7

C 7 and 8

D 39 and 41

6 Which integer is closest to $\sqrt{53}$?

A 6

B 7

C 8

D 9

Go On ➡

Brief Constructed Response

7 The area of a square is 78 square units. Tim wrote this expression for the length of a side of the square.

$\sqrt{78}$

Step A What whole number is closest to $\sqrt{78}$?

_____

Step B Use what you know about estimating square roots to explain why your answer is correct. Use words and/or numbers to support your explanation.

_____

_____

_____

_____

LESSON 33 Exponents

This lesson develops several rules for working with exponents.

6^3 stands for $6 \times 6 \times 6$, or in standard form, 216.

For 6^3 the number 6 is called the **base** and 3 is the **exponent** of 6.

6^3 can be read as 6 **to the third power**, or 6 **cubed**.

Example 1

Find the missing exponent n: $3^3 \times 3^4 = 3^n$

STRATEGY: **Show the complete multiplication.**

STEP 1: Write out the full multiplication for 3^3.

$3^3 = 3 \times 3 \times 3$

STEP 2: Write out the full multiplication for 3^4.

$3^4 = 3 \times 3 \times 3 \times 3$

STEP 3: Write out the full multiplication for $3^3 \times 3^4$.

$3^3 \times 3^4 = (3 \times 3 \times 3) \times (3 \times 3 \times 3 \times 3)$

STEP 4: Write the full multiplication in exponent form.

$(3 \times 3 \times 3) \times (3 \times 3 \times 3 \times 3) = 3^7$

SOLUTION: $3^3 \times 3^4 = 3^7$, so $n = 7$.

Example 1 illustrates this rule:

RULE 1: $a^s \times a^t = a^{s+t}$ for any number a and for integers s and t.

The rule says: **add** the exponents when multiplying two numbers in exponent form with the same base.

Example 2

Simplify $(-2)^2 \times (-2)^1$ and write the expression as a number in standard form.

STRATEGY: **Use Rule 1 to simplify.**

    STEP 1: $a^s \times a^t = a^{s+t}$

$$(-2)^2 \times (-2)^1 = (-2)^{2+1}$$
$$= (-2)^3$$

    STEP 2: Simplify the expression.
$$(-2)^3 = (-2) \times (-2) \times (-2)$$
$$= \quad (4) \quad \times (-2)$$
$$= -8$$

SOLUTION: $(-2)^2 \times (-2)^1 = (-2)^3 = -8.$

Example 3

Find the missing exponent n: $(4^5)^2 = 4^n$

STRATEGY: **Write the full multiplication for the outer exponent.**

    STEP 1: Write the full multiplication for the exponent of $(4^5)^2$.
$$(4^5)^2 = 4^5 \times 4^5$$

    STEP 2: Use Rule 1:
$$4^5 \times 4^5 = 4^{10}$$

SOLUTION: $(4^5)^2 = 4^{10}$, so $n = 10$.

Example 2 illustrates this rule:

> **RULE 2:** $(a^s)^t = a^{st}$ for any number a and for integers s and t.
>
> The rule says: **multiply** the exponents when raising a number with an exponent to a power.

Here is another rule you need to know:

> **RULE 3:** $\dfrac{a^s}{a^t} = a^{s-t}$ where a is any number and s and t are integers.
>
> The rule says: **subtract** the exponents when dividing two numbers in exponent form with the same base.

NOTE: If an exponent is not indicated, you may assume that the exponent is equal to 1. ($y = y^1$ and $z = z^1$)

Example 4

Find n for $\dfrac{6^5}{6^2} = 6^n$

STRATEGY: Use Rule 3.

$$\frac{6^5}{6^2} = 6^{5-2} = 6^3$$

SOLUTION: So, $n = 3$

Sample Test Questions

1 $7^3 = ?$

A 10
B 21
C 49
D 343

2 $(-12)^2 = ?$

A −144
B −24
C 24
D 144

3 $2^3 \times 3^3 = ?$

A 35
B 54
C 125
D 216

4 $9^2 \times 9^1 = ?$

A 9^1
B 9^2
C 9^3
D 9^4

5 $(2^3)^3 = ?$

A 2^3
B 2^6
C 2^9
D 2^{27}

6 $(4^3)^4 = ?$

A 4^1
B 4^7
C 4^{12}
D 4^{16}

7 $(-3) \times (-3)^2 = ?$

A −3
B $(-3)^2$
C $(-3)^3$
D −9

8 $7^5 \div 7^2 = ?$

A 7^3
B 7^7
C 7^{10}
D 7^{25}

9 $\frac{5^4}{5^2} = ?$

A 5^{16}
B 5^8
C 5^6
D 5^2

Go On ➡

10 Find n: $(5^2)^4 = 5^n$

   A   8

   B   6

   C   4

   D   2

11 Find n: $10^7 \div 10^1 = 10^n$

   A   6

   B   7

   C   8

   D   10

12 Write 8^3 as a standard numeral.

Go On ➡

Extended Constructed Response

13 Ray used the numerals 5, 8, and 9 to write this expression:

$$\frac{9^8}{9^5}$$

Step A Write an expression equivalent to Ray's expression using the base 9 and just one exponent.

_____

_____

Go On ➡

Step B • Use what you know about expressions with exponents to explain why your answer is correct. Use words and/or numbers to support your explanation.

_____

_____

_____

_____

• Write the expression you found in Step A as a number in standard form. Use words and/or numbers to explain how you found the standard form.

_____

_____

_____

_____

Standard 6.C.1.d

LESSON
34 Properties of Numbers

There are a number of math rules that you need to know in order to do algebra problems. These rules are often called **properties**. Here are some of the properties you should know.

Addition Properties

Commutative Property of Addition

Numbers can be added in any order. The sum will be the same.

$a + b = b + a$

Associative Property of Addition

Addends can be grouped in different ways. The sum will be the same.

$(a + b) + c = a + (b + c)$

Identity Property of Addition

If you add 0 to any number, the sum will be that number.

$a + 0 = a$ or $0 + a = a$

Additive Inverse Property

The additive inverse of a number is the opposite of that number. The sum of a number and its additive inverse is 0.

$a + (-a) = 0$ or $-a + a = 0$

Multiplication Properties

Commutative Property of Multiplication

Numbers can be multiplied in any order. The product will be the same.

$a \times b = b \times a$

Associative Property of Multiplication

Factors can be grouped in different ways. The product will be the same.

$(a \times b) \times c = a \times (b \times c)$

Identity Property of Multiplication

When one of two factors is 1, the product will be the other factor.

$a \times 1 = a \quad or \quad 1 \times a = a$

Zero Property of Multiplication

When one of two factors is 0, the product will be 0.

$a \times 0 = 0 \quad or \quad 0 \times a = 0$

Multiplication and Addition Property

Distributive Property of Multiplication over Addition

$a \times (b + c) = a \times b + a \times c$

Example 1

Which property will make this computation simpler?

$9 \times 37 + 9 \times 3$

STRATEGY: **Look for a number property that applies to the computation, and see if it makes things simpler.**

STEP 1: Recognize that the computation involves both multiplication and addition, which suggests the distributive property.

STEP 2: Recognize also that the distributive property works both ways. That is, it can be stated as

$a \times b + a \times c = a \times (b + c)$

STEP 3: Apply this version of the distributive property to the computation.

$9 \times 37 + 9 \times 3 = 9 \times (37 + 3)$

STEP 4: Add the numbers in the parentheses.

$9 \times (37 + 3) = 9 \times 40$

The computation becomes simpler:

Instead of $9 \times 37 + 9 \times 3$, we just multiply 9×40.

SOLUTION: **$9 \times 40 = 360$. The distributive property made the computation simpler.**

Example 2

Simplify this expression: $87 + (25 + (-87))$

STRATEGY: **Apply the properties.**

$87 + (25 + (-87))$	
$(25 + (-87)) + 87$	Commutative Property of Addition (Change the order of 87 and $(25 + (-87))$)
$25 + ((-87) + 87)$	Associative Property of Addition
$25 + 0$	Additive Inverse Property
25	Identity Property of Addition

SOLUTION: **The answer is 25.**

Sample Test Questions

1 If $a + b = c$, then which of the following is true?

A $b - c = a$

B $a = b + c$

C $b \times a = c$

D $b + a = c$

2 What expression is equivalent to $a \times (b + c)$?

A $a \times b + c$

B $a \times b + a \times c$

C $a + b \times c$

D $a \times b \times c$

3 Which shows the associative property for multiplication?

A $(9 \times 2) \times 5 = 9 \times (2 \times 5)$

B $(9 \times 2) \times 5 = 9 \times (2 + 5)$

C $(9 \times 2) \times 5 = 5 \times (9 \times 2)$

D $9 \times (2 \times 5) = 9 \times (5 \times 2)$

4 If you wanted to find the answer to this computation mentally, what property would you use?

$$-8 \times 7 + -8 \times 3$$

A Associative Property of Multiplication

B Distributive Property of Multiplication over Addition

C Identity Property of Multiplication

D Commutative Property of Multiplication

5 Which of the ways of rewriting the computation below would make it easier to compute?

$$-43 + 19 + 43$$

A $2 \times 43 + 19$

B $-43 + (19 + 43)$

C $-43 + 43 + 19$

D $43 (-1 + 19)$

6 Which property is used in the following equation?

$$7(-4 + 8) = 7(-4) + 7(8)$$

A Associative Property of Addition

B Associative Property of Multiplication

C Distributive Property of Multiplication over Addition

D Identity Property of Addition

7 Which expression is equivalent to $3 \times 5 + 12$?

A $3(5 + 4)$

B $3(5 + 2)$

C $3(5 + 12)$

D $3(5 + 36)$

Go On ➡

206

8 Which property is used in the following equation?

$$(9 + 7) + (21 + 3) = (21 + 3) + (9 + 7)$$

A Associative Property of Addition

B Commutative Property of Addition

C Identity Property of Addition

D Distributive Property of Multiplication over Addition

9 Which property would you use to find this sum?

$$(-93) + 93 = ?$$

A Identity Property of Addition

B Additive Inverse Property

C Commutative Property of Addition

D Associative Property of Addition

10 Which expression is the same as $(-9 \times 8) + (-9 \times 2)$?

A $-9 \times (8 + 2)$

B $-9 \times (8 \times 2)$

C $(-9 + 8) \times 2$

D $(-9 \times 8) + 2$

11 Which of these expressions is NOT true?

A $-24 + 0 = -24$

B $1 \times 73 = 73$

C $0 \times 4 = 4$

D $0 + 26 = 26 + 0$

Go On ➡

Brief Constructed Response

12 Willie substituted values into the formula for the perimeter of a rectangle and got this expression:

$2 \times 39 + 2 \times 11$

Step A Name a property that can be used to simplify the expression so that you can do the math mentally. Then simplify the expression using that property.

_____

_____

_____

Step B Use what you know about number properties to explain why your answer is correct. Use words and/or numbers to support your explanation.

_____

_____

_____

_____

_____

LESSON 35 Estimation

We frequently **estimate** when we communicate numerical information.

Example 1

Last year Kevin made $204 per week at his job. This year he got a raise of $27 per week. What is a good estimate of the rate of increase in his weekly pay?

STRATEGY: **Find numbers close to 204 and 27 that form a fraction that is easy to convert into a percent.**

STEP 1: Find numbers that are close to 204 and 27.

$$204 \approx 200 \text{ and } 27 \approx 30$$

STEP 2: Write a fraction and convert it to a percent.

$$\text{Rate of increase} = \frac{\text{amount of increase}}{\text{original amount}} = \frac{30}{200} = \frac{15}{100} = 15\%$$

SOLUTION: **A good estimate of the rate of increase is 15%.**

Example 2

Joanna figures that she saves 27 percent when she shops at the supermarket instead of at the deli. Last Thursday she spent $83 at the deli. If she had shopped at the supermarket, about how much money would she have saved?

STRATEGY: **Use rounding.**

STEP 1: Round the percent to the nearest 10.

27 percent becomes 30 percent.

STEP 2: Round the amount purchased to the nearest 10.

$83 becomes $80.

STEP 3: Compute the amount of money saved using the rounded numbers.

$$30\% \text{ of } 80 = 0.30 \times 80 = 24$$

SOLUTION: **The amount saved is about $24.**

Sample Test Questions

1 Sam sells real estate. He earns a 3% commission on each property he sells. About how much will his commission be if he sells a lot for $4,150?

A $60

B $120

C $1,150

D $1,200

2 If the sales tax is 5%, which is the best estimate of the amount of sales tax on a refrigerator that costs $786?

A $400

B $50

C $40

D $30

3 A television that regularly sells for $209 is put on sale at a discount of 30%. About how much is the discount?

A $30

B $60

C $80

D $90

4 In the year 1990, the population of the town where Cindy lives was 1507. By the year 2000, there were 148 fewer people in the town. What is a good estimate of the rate of decease in the population?

A 5%

B 10%

C 15%

D 20%

5 Neal has $5,100 to invest. What is a good estimate of the amount of simple interest he can earn if he invests the money for 2 years at a rate of 4%?

A $40

B $100

C $200

D $400

Go On ➡

Brief Constructed Response

6 In the year 1990, the population of a city was 7,936. By the year 2000, the population had increased by 397.

Step A What is a good estimate of the percent of increase in population?

_____

Step B Use what you know about estimating percents to explain why your estimate is good. Use words and/or numbers to support your explanation.

_____

_____

_____

_____

_____

LESSON 36 Unit Price

When you buy many items that are the same, it is good to know what each one costs. Or, if you shop for different brands, it makes sense to be able to compare the prices of the different brands. A good way to compare is to find the unit price—the price of one item or one unit of measure.

Method 1 for Finding the Unit Price

To find the unit price for a set of items, divide the total cost by the number of items.

Method 2 for Finding the Unit Price

To find the unit price of an item of a given weight or capacity, divide the total cost by the number of units of weight or capacity.

Example 1

Jenny spent $3.20 for 8 donuts. What is the unit price for these donuts?

STRATEGY: **Use Method 1.**

STEP 1: What is the cost of the donuts?

The total cost is $3.20.

STEP 2: How many donuts did Jenny buy?

She bought 8 donuts.

STEP 3: Use the method above for finding the unit price.

Divide $3.20 by 8.

Change $3.20 to cents: $3.20 is the same as 320 cents.

$$
\begin{array}{r}
40 \\
8\overline{)320} \\
-32 \\
\hline
00 \\
00 \\
\hline
\end{array}
$$

$$320 \div 8 = 40$$

SOLUTION: **The unit price is 40 cents. This means that a single donut costs 40 cents.**

Finding the unit prices of two similar items is often a good way to compare the value of the items.

Example 2

Compare the unit values of these two cans of soup, and determine which is the better value.

> Brand A Tomato Soup weighs 14 ounces and costs $2.40.
>
> Brand B Tomato Soup weighs 12 ounces and costs $2.15.

STRATEGY: **Find the unit price of each by using Method 2, and compare.**

STEP 1: Find the unit price of Brand A Soup.

Divide the cost of Brand A Soup by the weight:

$2.40 ÷ 14, or in cents, 240 ÷ 14 = 17.1 cents per ounce.

STEP 2: Find the unit price of Brand B Soup.

Divide the cost of Brand B Soup by the weight:
$2.15 ÷ 12, or in cents, 215 ÷ 12 = 17.9 cents per ounce.

STEP 3: Compare the prices.

SOLUTION: **Brand A is less expensive—it costs 17.1 cents per ounce compared to 17.9 cents for Brand B.**

Sample Test Questions

For Questions 1–4, find the unit price of each product. Round if necessary.

1 A dozen tomatoes costs $1.56.

    A 11 cents per tomato

    B 12 cents per tomato

    C 13 cents per tomato

    D 14 cents per tomato

2 A 17-ounce package of spaghetti costs $4.12.

    A 24 cents per ounce

    B 26 cents per ounce

    C 28 cents per ounce

    D 30 cents per ounce

3 A gallon container of apple juice sells for $4.80.

    A $1.20 per pint

    B $1.00 per pint

    C $0.60 per pint

    D $0.40 per pint

4 A package of 100 sheets of paper costs $1.50.

    A 1 cent per sheet

    B $1\frac{1}{2}$ cents per sheet

    C 2 cents per sheet

    D $2\frac{1}{2}$ cents per sheet

5 A package of 20 slices of Komak American cheese costs $1.80. A package of 24 slices of Modak American cheese costs $2.64. Which cheese is the better value and by how much?

    A Komak   2 cents per slice

    B Komak   4 cents per slice

    C Modak   2 cents per slice

    D Modak   4 cents per slice

6 A box of 40 pencils from Harrow's Pencil Company costs $6.80, while a box of 50 pencils from the Carbon Pencil Company costs $9.00. Which box of pencils is the better value and by how much?

    A Harrow   2 cents

    B Harrow   1 cent

    C Carbon   2 cents

    D Carbon   1 cent

7 What is the unit price to the nearest cent of a 33-ounce bottle of juice that sells for $2.99?

Go On ➡

214

Brief Constructed Response

8 Brand A pasta sauce weighs 26 ounces and costs $4.99. Brand B pasta sauce weighs 32 ounces and costs $5.79.

Step A   Which brand of pasta sauce is the better buy?

_____

Step B   Use what you know about unit rates to explain why your answer is correct. Use words and/or numbers to support your explanation.

_____

_____

_____

_____

STOP

215

LESSON 37 Applications of Percents

This lesson will apply the methods of finding percents to problems.

Example 1

Jonah's father is a car salesman. He receives a 5% commission for every car he sells. How much commission does he earn if he sells a car for $22,000?

STRATEGY: **Change the percent to a decimal and multiply.**

    STEP 1: Change 5% to a decimal.

            5% = 0.05

    STEP 2: Use the decimal and multiply to find the commission.

            $0.05 \times 22{,}000 = 1{,}100$

SOLUTION: **The amount of commission is $1,100.**

Example 2

The Lanax Company showed a profit of $2,000,000 last year. This year a 12% increase in profit is expected. What would the profit be this year if the expectation turns out to be correct?

STRATEGY: **Think of this as a percent increase problem.**

    STEP 1: Change the rate to a decimal.

            rate = 12% = 0.12

    STEP 2: Find the amount of increase.

            $0.12 \times 2{,}000{,}000 = \$240{,}000$

    STEP 3: Add the amount of increase to last year's profits.

            $2{,}000{,}000 + 240{,}000 = 2{,}240{,}000$

SOLUTION: **The profit this year would be $2,240,000.**

Example 3

A CD that regularly costs $18.50 goes on sale at 40% off the regular price. What is the sale price?

STRATEGY: **Change the percent to a decimal and multiply. Subtract the product from the regular price.**

        STEP 1: Change rate of discount to a decimal.

              40% = 0.4

        STEP 2: Multiply.

              $18.50 × 0.4 = $7.40

        STEP 3: Subtract the discount from the regular price.

              $18.50 − $7.40 = $11.10

SOLUTION: **The sale price is $11.10.**

Simple interest is an important use of percents.

Formula for Simple Interest $i = Prt$

Where i is the interest earned, P is the principal or amount invested, r is the rate as a decimal, and t is the number of years the money is invested.

Example 4

The Alfonso family owns a restaurant. Since business has been good, they want to make improvements in the restaurant. They borrow $100,000 from a bank at 7% interest over 10 years. How much total interest will they pay?

STRATEGY: **Use the formula for simple interest.**

        STEP 1: Change the rate to a decimal.

              $r = 7\% = 0.07$

        STEP 2: Substitute in the formula for simple interest.

              $i = Prt = 100{,}000 × 0.07 × 10 = 70{,}000$

SOLUTION: **The interest the Alfonso family will pay over 10 years is $70,000.**

Sample Test Questions

1 Find the amount of interest that will be earned on an investment of $8,000 at 10% simple interest for 3 years.

A $2,400

B $2,500

C $2,600

D $2,800

2 Jennifer is a textbook salesperson. Last week her sales were $9,000. How much commission will she make for the week if her rate of commission is 14%?

A $2,520

B $1,260

C $1,080

D $960

3 The Norris Depot Company decided to "mark-up" the price of one of its popular pieces of outdoor furniture—a table with wheels. (Mark-up means to raise the price.) This table now sells for $145, but starting next month the company will sell it for 15% more. What will be the new price?

A $150.75

B $155.75

C $166.75

D $170.75

4 If the rate of sales tax is 6%, what is the sales tax on a computer that costs $1,450?

A $8.70

B $77

C $87

D $97

5 A television has a regular price of $215. It goes on sale at a 20% discount. What is the amount of the discount?

A $4.30

B $43

C $53.75

D $107.50

6 Last year there were 540 eighth graders in the Springfield school system. This year, the number of eighth graders decreased by 15%. How many fewer eighth graders are there this year?

Go On ➡

Brief Constructed Response

7 Gail makes $750 per week at her job. Next week, she will get a 3% raise.

Step A How much more will she make next week?

_____

Step B Use what you know about applying percents to explain why your answer is correct. Use words and/or numbers to support your explanation.

_____

_____

_____

_____

_____

LESSON

38 Using Proportions

Proportions are useful in solving a variety of problems.

Example 1

A girl who is 4 feet tall casts a shadow of 3 feet. If a flagpole is 20 feet high, what is the length of the shadow of the flagpole?

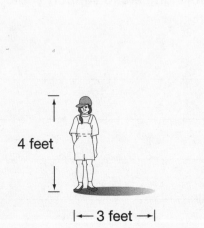

4 feet

|← 3 feet →|

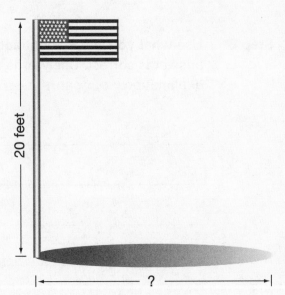

20 feet

|← ? →|

STRATEGY: **Set up a proportion and solve it.**

STEP 1: Set up a ratio for the girl and her shadow.

$$\frac{\text{height}}{\text{shadow}} = \frac{4}{3}$$

STEP 2: Set up a ratio for the flagpole.

$$\frac{\text{height}}{\text{shadow}} = \frac{20}{F}$$

where F stands for the length of the flagpole's shadow.

STEP 3: Set up a proportion with the two ratios.

$$\frac{4}{3} = \frac{20}{F}$$

220

STEP 4: Solve for F, the length of the shadow of the flagpole.

Cross-multiply in the proportion of Step 3:

$4 \times F = 60$

Solve for F: $F = 15$

SOLUTION: **The length of the shadow of the flagpole is 15 feet.**

Example 2

Chris measured the distance on a map from his house to his cousin Franklin's house. It is 3.5 inches. On the map, the key shows that 1 inch = 200 miles. How far away does Franklin live from Chris?

STRATEGY: **Set up a proportion and solve it.**

STEP 1: What is the scale from the map?

$$\text{Scale} = \frac{1 \text{ inch}}{200 \text{ miles}}$$

STEP 2: Set up a proportion using the scale.

$$\frac{1 \text{ inch}}{200 \text{ miles}} = \frac{\text{distance on map}}{\text{actual distance}}$$

STEP 3: Substitute in the proportion.

$$\frac{1 \text{ inch}}{200 \text{ miles}} = \frac{3.5 \text{ inches}}{\text{actual distance}} = \frac{3.5 \text{ inches}}{D}$$

(D = actual distance)

STEP 4: Solve the proportion.

$D = 200 \times 3.5 = 700$ miles

SOLUTION: **Franklin lives 700 miles away from Chris.**

Sample Test Questions

1 Henderson said that his team wins 2 out of every 5 games. If the team plays 35 games this season, which proportion can be used to determine W, the number of wins expected at the end of the season?

A $\frac{2}{5} = \frac{35}{W}$

B $\frac{5}{2} = \frac{W}{35}$

C $\frac{2}{5} = \frac{W}{35}$

D $\frac{2}{5} = W - \frac{2}{35}$

2 A 12-foot tree casts a shadow of 4 feet. How long is the shadow of a school building that is 40 feet tall?

A 10 feet   C 12 feet

B $12\frac{1}{4}$ feet   D $13\frac{1}{3}$ feet

3 A map shows a scale of 2 in. = 40 miles. What is the distance between two cities that are 9 in. apart on the map?

A 180 miles

B 170 miles

C 160 miles

D 150 miles

4 Jack says he makes $70 for every 5 hours he works. How much money does he make after he works 25 hours?

A $400   C $350

B $375   D $325

5 Every 3 weeks, the Kerner family drinks 24 bottles of juice. At this rate, how many bottles of juice will the family drink in 10 weeks?

A 90   C 80

B 85   D 70

6 Kim's father drove 300 miles to Baltimore at an average rate of 45 miles per hour. How long did it take him to get to Baltimore?

A $5\frac{2}{3}$ hours   C $6\frac{1}{3}$ hours

B 6 hours   D $6\frac{2}{3}$ hours

7 Norma receives an average of 20 e-mail messages every three days. How many e-mail messages can she expect to receive in one month? (1 month = 30 days)

A 100

B 150

C 200

D 250

Go On ➡

222

Brief Constructed Response

8 On a blueprint of Monica's house, the length of her living room is 5 inches. The scale on the blueprint is $\frac{1}{4}$ in. = 1 ft.

Step A What is the actual length of Monica's living room?

_____

Step B Use what you know about setting up and solving proportions to explain why your answer is correct. Use words, numbers, and/or diagrams to support your explanation.

_____

_____

_____

_____

_____

Standard 6.0: Number Relationships and Computation

Progress Check for Lessons 29–38

1 When the planet Mars is farthest away from Earth, it is 249,000,000 miles away. What is this distance in scientific notation?

A 249×10^6 miles

B 24.9×10^7 miles

C 2.49×10^8 miles

D 2.49×10^{-8} miles

2 One yard is approximately 0.000568 mile. What is this decimal in scientific notation?

A 5.68×10^4

B 5.68×10^{-4}

C 5.68×10^5

D 5.68×10^{-5}

3 Which is the least of these numbers?

A 0

B 7

C −8

D $|-9|$

4 Which list shows these numbers from least to greatest?

$$0.\overline{12}, \frac{1}{9}, 0.1, 0.12$$

A $0.1, \frac{1}{9}, 0.12, 0.\overline{12}$

B $0.1, \frac{1}{9}, 0.\overline{12}, 0.12$

C $0.\overline{12}, 0.12, \frac{1}{9}, 0.1$

D $0.\overline{12}, 0.12, 0.1, \frac{1}{9}$

5 $(-250) - (-150) = ?$

A −400

B −100

C 100

D 400

6 $(-8) \times (-6) \times (-5) = ?$

A −240

B −21

C 21

D 240

7 $(-90) \div (-18) = ?$

A −72

B −5

C 5

D 72

Go On ➡

8 $(-17) + 30 = ?$

A −47   C 13

B −13   D 47

9 Find $\sqrt{64}$.

A 32   C 8

B 16   D 4

10 Which integer is closest to $\sqrt{67}$?

A 6   C 8

B 7   D 9

11 $12^3 = ?$

A 15   C 144

B 36   D 1,728

12 $(3^2)^3 = ?$

A 3^1 C 3^6

B 3^5 D 3^8

13 Which expression is equivalent to $4 \times 3 + 20$?

A $4(3 + 16)$

B $4(3 + 20)$

C $4(3 + 5)$

D $4(3 + 80)$

14 If the sales tax is 6%, about how much tax would you pay for a used car that costs $8,995?

A $270   C $540

B $460   D $9,540

15 An 18-ounce package of lentils costs $1.79. What is the unit price to the nearest cent?

A $0.08 per ounce

B $0.09 per ounce

C $0.10 per ounce

D $0.11 per ounce

16 A map has the scale 0.5 in. = 8 mi. What is the actual distance between two cities that are 4.5 inches apart on the map?

A 5 miles   C 17 miles

B 9 miles   D 72 miles

17 In the year 2000, the population of a town was 7,650. By the year 2004, the population had increased by 18%. How many more people lived in the town in 2004?

Go On ➡

Standard 6.0: Number Relationships and Computation

Constructed Response Questions

Brief Constructed Response

18   José paid $72 for a baseball glove. This was 10% less than the regular price because he bought it online.

Step A   What was the original price of the glove?

_____

Step B   Use what you know about applying percents to explain why your answer is correct. Use words and/or numbers to support your explanation.

_____

_____

_____

_____

_____

Go On ➡

Extended Constructed Response

19   Keisha researched the annual budget of her town and discovered that it was 32,800,000 dollars.

Step A   Write this number in scientific notation.

_____

_____

Step B   • Use what you know about writing numbers in scientific notation to explain why your answer is correct.

_____

_____

_____

•   Suppose Keisha made a mistake and the budget was 10 times as great as the number she recorded. How would you have to change your answer in Step A to show the new number in scientific notation? Explain your steps.

_____

_____

_____

20 At 2:00 P.M. the temperature was 3°C. By 10:00 P.M., the temperature had fallen 7°C.

Step A What was the temperature at 10:00 P.M.?

_____

Step B
- Use what you know about working with integers to explain why your answer is correct. Use words, numbers, and/or pictures to support your explanation.

_____

_____

_____

_____

- On the next morning the temperature rose 9°C. What was the temperature the next morning? How does this temperature compare with the temperature at 2:00 the day before? Explain using words, numbers, and/or pictures.

_____

_____

_____

_____

Go On ➡

21 A box of Cereal A contains 18 ounces and costs $4.99. A box of Cereal B contains 16 ounces and costs $4.79.

Step A   Which cereal is the better buy?

_____

Step B   • Use what you know about unit prices to explain why your answer is correct. Use words and/or numbers to support your explanation.

_____

_____

_____

_____

• Suppose you decide to manufacture Cereal C to compete with the other two cereals. Choose: a unit price, the number of ounces in the box, and a selling price. Explain your strategy.

_____

_____

_____

_____

Mathematical Processes

In this unit you will learn about solving problems. There are many different strategies that you can use to solve problems, but you should always follow the same basic steps.

Try This

You will need:

- a partner
- paper and pencil
- grid paper
- calculator (optional)

Follow these steps:

1. Study this problem:

   Rosa walked 3 meters east, then 2 meters north, then 2 meters east, then 6 meters north, then 1 meter east. How far is she from the place she started?

2. Work with your partner to come up with a strategy for solving the problem. How might a person be misled from the information in the problem? How can drawing a picture help you solve this problem?

3. What fact from geometry can you use to find the distance?

4. Work with your partner to solve the problem. Compare your results with another pair of students.

5. Write a problem similar to the given one. Solve it. Then give it to another pair to solve.

Think about it:

What other problems can be solved using a drawing?

What kinds of problems are not appropriate for a making-a-drawing strategy?

LESSON 39 Using a 4-Step Method to Solve Problems

Here is a simple 4-step method to help solve problems:

> **STEP 1:** **Read the problem carefully.**
> What are you trying to find?
>
> **STEP 2:** **Plan what you are going to do.**
> What do you know?
> What operation should you use?
>
> **STEP 3:** **Carry out the plan.**
>
> **STEP 4:** **Check the answer.**

Example 1

Belinda bought three books and two calculators as gifts for her friends. She paid $17.50 for each book. Each calculator costs the same amount. All together, Belinda spent $77.50. How much did each calculator cost?

STRATEGY: Follow the 4-step approach above.

STEP 1: Read the problem carefully.

What are you trying to find?
The cost of each calculator.

STEP 2: Plan what you are going to do.

What do you know?
The total cost of three books and two calculators is $77.50.
The cost of each book is $17.50.

What operation should you use?

Two operations: First multiply to find the total cost of the books. Then subtract to find the cost of two calculators. Finally, divide the cost of the two calculators by 2.

STEP 3:   Carry out the plan.

Cost of books: $3 \times 17.50 = \$52.50$

Cost of two calculators: $\$77.50 - 52.50 = \$25$

Cost of each calculator: $\$25 \div 2 = \$12.50$

STEP 4:   Check the answer.

$12.50 \times 2 = 25$

$25 + 52.50 = 77.50$

$52.50 \div 3 = 17.50$

SOLUTION: Each calculator costs $12.50.

Using the 4-step approach can help you analyze a problem to decide if there is enough information to solve the problem.

Example 2

Juan earns $12 per hour for the first 40 hours he works in a week. He earns $1\frac{1}{2}$ times his hourly pay in overtime for each hour he works over 40 hours in a week. Last week, Juan worked overtime. How much did Juan earn last week? What additional information do you need to solve this problem?

STRATEGY: Use Steps 1 and 2 of the 4-step method.

STEP 1:   Read the problem carefully.

What are you trying to find?

The amount of money Juan earned last week.

STEP 2:   Plan what you are going to do.

What do you know?

He earns $12 per hour for the first 40 hours.

He earns $1\frac{1}{2}$ times $12, or $18, per hour for any hours over 40.

What operation should you use?

First find two products:

Multiply $12 by 40 to find the amount earned in the first 40 hours.

Multiply $18 by the number of hours over 40.

Then add the two products.

The problem does not indicate the number of hours over 40 he worked.

SOLUTION: You need to know the total number of hours Juan worked.

Sample Test Questions

1 After playing 10 basketball games, Julie's average is 13 points per game. If her average for the first 5 games is 10 points, what is her average for the last 5 games?

A 12   C 16
B 14   D 18

2 A new bridge in Steventown is 1.2 km long. How many meters long is this?

A 12,000   C 120
B 1,200   D 12

3 Each chocolate candy costs 65 cents. If Peter buys a dozen, how much change will he get from $10?

A $3.20   C $2.60
B $2.80   D $2.20

4 Of the 1,400 cars that drove into downtown Steventown yesterday, 35% parked in or near the downtown area. How many cars was that?

A 450

B 470

C 480

D 490

5 Morris bought an antique chair for $400 and sold it last week for $800. What is the percent profit that he made on this chair?

A 50%   C 150%
B 100%   D 200%

6 Doreen estimates that each month she sends $\frac{1}{10}$ more e-mail messages than she did the month before. If she sent 1,000 messages in January, how many messages did she send in March?

A 1,100

B 1,210

C 1,331

D not enough information

7 This year, there are 408 students enrolled at Stevens High School. This is 1.2 times the number of students enrolled last year. How many students were enrolled last year?

Go On ➡

234

Extended Constructed Response

8 Maria left her house and walked for 25 minutes to get to Karen's house. After visiting with Karen for $1\frac{1}{4}$ hours, she walked for 15 minutes to get to the market. After spending 10 minutes at the market, she walked for 20 minutes to get home. At what time did she get home?

Step A   What additional information do you need to solve this problem?

_____

_____

_____

Step B   • Use what you know about using information in a problem to explain why your answer is correct. Use words and/or numbers to support your explanation.

_____

_____

_____

• Provide information so that the problem can be solved. Then solve the problem using the 4-step method. Explain each step.

_____

_____

_____

Standards 7.A.1.d, e, 7.C.1.e

40 Strategies for Problem Solving

You should know about these strategies for solving problems:

STRATEGIES

1 Act it out
2 Make a model
3 Draw a picture
4 Make a chart or graph
5 Look for a pattern
6 Make a simpler problem
7 Use logic
8 Work backward
9 Guess and check
10 Break into parts

Example 1

Steve lives 6 miles from Darrell, and Darrell lives 4 miles from Donna. Which of the following is NOT a possible distance between Steve and Donna?

A 2 miles **C** 10 miles

B 4 miles **D** 12 miles

STRATEGY: **Choose the strategy that best fits this problem.**

STEP 1: Read the problem several times. Then look at the list of strategies above. Ask yourself: Which strategy would help me solve this problem?

One of the best strategies for this type of problem is "**Draw a picture.**" This is a good strategy, since you have a better chance of solving the problem if you see the three locations on paper.

You will have to draw several pictures, since there is more than one way that the houses can be set up.

Duplicating any part of this book is forbidden by law.

STEP 2: Draw a picture.

Here is one picture of the three places in the problem.

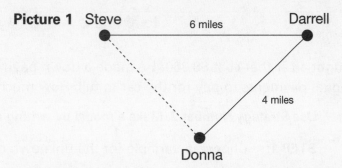

Picture 1

From Picture 1, you can see that the distance from Steve to Donna could be 4 miles. So, Answer B is possible.

STEP 3: Draw another picture of the three places.

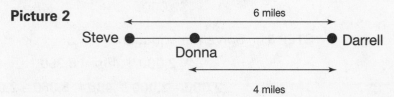

Picture 2

Picture 2 shows us that the 3 places can be on the same line. Here, Donna lives 2 miles from Steve ($6 - 4 = 2$). Answer A is possible.

STEP 4: Draw another picture.

Picture 3

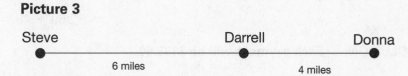

Picture 3 shows us another way that the locations can be on the same line. In this case, the distance between Donna and Steve is 10 miles. Answer C is possible.

This is also the greatest distance Steve can live from Donna.

We eliminated answers B, A, and C—all are possible.

STEP 5: Ask: Do you need to draw any more pictures?

No. We've already eliminated answers A, B, and C. We can't eliminate Answer D as a possibility, since 10 miles was the farthest Steve could live from Donna.

SOLUTION: **Answer D is not possible as the distance between Steve and Donna. Donna cannot be more than 10 miles from Steve (see Picture 3).**

237

Sometimes you can model a problem by writing an equation.

Example 2

Darren bought a car that cost $8,360. He made a down payment of $2,000 and will make 48 equal payments to pay for the car in full. How much will each payment be?

STRATEGY: **Use Strategy Number 2. Make a model by writing an equation.**

STEP 1:   Choose a variable for the unknown quantity, the payment.

Let p stand for each payment.

STEP 2:   Translate the problem into an equation.

Down payment + 48 × each payment = total cost

$2,000   +   48$p$ = 8,360

STEP 3:   Solve the equation.

$$2,000 + 48p = 8,360$$

$$2,000 - 2,000 + 48p = 8,360 - 2,000 \text{ Subtract 2,000 from}$$
$$\text{each side.}$$

$$0 + 48p = 6,360$$

$$\tfrac{1}{48} \times (48p) = \tfrac{1}{48} \times (6,360) \text{ Multiply each side by } \tfrac{1}{48}.$$

$$p = \tfrac{6360}{48}$$

$$= 6,360 \div 48 = 132.5$$

SOLUTION: **Each payment will be $132.50.**

Sample Test Questions

1 Michelle is trying to find the next number in this sequence:

1, 7, 13, 19, 25, 31, ____

Which of the following would most help Michelle to solve this problem?

A Make a model

B Draw a picture

C Break into parts

D Look for a pattern

2 Harold asked his friend George if he knows how many diagonals can be drawn in a polygon with 10 sides (called a decagon). Which of the following would help George the most in solving this problem?

A Act it out

B Guess and check

C Work backward

D Draw a picture

3 Mrs. Jones asked 6 children to figure out how many handshakes there would be if all 6 children shook hands with each other. Which of the following would help most to solve this problem?

A Act it out

B Make a graph

C Work backward

D Guess and check

4 What is the area of the region enclosed by the figure below?

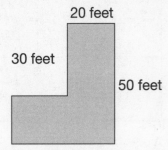

20 feet

30 feet

50 feet

40 feet

A 1,040 square feet

B 1,200 square feet

C 1,400 square feet

D 1,600 square feet

Go On ➡

5 Samantha puts money in her bank every day. On Monday she put in $1, on Tuesday she put in $2, on Wednesday she put in $4, on Thursday she put in $8, and on Friday she put in $16. If she continues in the same way, how much money will she put in her bank on Saturday?

A $20   C $30

B $25   D $32

6 How many total squares are there in this grid?

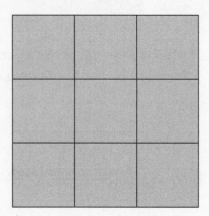

A 9

B 12

C 14

D 16

7 City A is 6 miles away from City B. If City C is 2 miles away from City B, what is a possible distance between City A and City C?

A 1 mile

B 2 miles

C 3 miles

D 4 miles

8 Carol has 8 cents more in her change purse than Joan has in her change purse. Carol has less than 12 cents in her change purse. How much money does Joan have in her purse?

A 4 cents

B 3 cents

C 3 or 4 cents

D 0, 1, 2, or 3 cents

9 Keith is three times as old as Lenny, and Matt is four times as old as Lenny. In 5 years from now, the sum of Keith and Matt's ages will be 40. Which equation cannot be used to model and solve this problem?

A $3x + 4x = 40 - 5$

B $3x + 4x = 40 + 5$

C $3x + 4x + 5 = 40$

D $7x + 5 = 40$

10 How many 8's do you have to write if you write the numbers from 1 to 99?

Go On ➡

Extended Constructed Response

11 Rosa has already saved $15 toward spending money for her summer vacation. She can save $8 per week. She wants to have at least $50 in spending money for her vacation.

Step A   Write a mathematical sentence to model this problem.

_____

_____

_____

Step B • Use what you know about problem solving strategies to explain why your answer is correct. Use words and/or numbers to support your explanation.

_____

_____

_____

• Suppose a classmate answered Step A with this inequality: $8x + 15 < 50$. What error did the classmate make? How would you explain to the classmate how to correct the error?

_____

_____

_____

LESSON 41
Solving Problems in More Than One Way

Some problems can be solved in more than one way. You may solve a problem one way, and a friend may solve the same problem another way.

Example 1

Jessica ran around the track 6 times. Each time around the track is 440 yards.

To find how far she ran, Jessica added: 440 + 440 + 440 + 440 + 440 + 440. What is another way to find how far she ran?

STRATEGY: **Read the problem again.**

SOLUTION: **Since she ran the same distance 6 times, another way to solve this problem is to multiply: 6 × 440.**

Example 2

A van from the mall costs $2 for the first mile and $0.75 for each mile after the first mile. How can you figure out how much it costs to travel 6 miles?

    A 6 × $0.75

    B $2 + 5 × $0.75

    C $2 + 6 × $0.75

    D 5 × $0.75

STRATEGY: **Think of the cost of the van in two parts, $2 and $0.75.**

                The first mile cost $2, and the other 5 miles cost $0.75 each.

                So, the total cost is $2 + the cost of the 5 miles.

SOLUTION: **The answer is $2 + 5 × $0.75, Answer B.**

Sample Test Questions

1 Melanie charges $4 an hour to babysit. Which of the following shows a way of finding how many hours she must work to earn $64?

A $64 \div 4$

B 64×4

C $64 - 4$

D $64 \div (2 + 4)$

2 It will take Dan 3 hours and 10 minutes to drive from home to the airport. It will take him another 40 minutes to get to the gate. He figures he needs 3 hours all together to get from his home to the gate. Is he correct?

A No, because 3 hours and 10 minutes + 40 minutes = 4 hours.

B Yes, because 3 hours and 10 minutes + 40 minutes is less than 3 hours.

C Yes, because 3 hours and 10 minutes + 40 minutes = 3 hours.

D No, because 3 hours and 10 minutes + 40 minutes is more than 3 hours.

3 The cost of a special ice cream at the mall is $2.25. Kathy's father paid for 3 special ice creams. Kathy figured that the cost was $5.75. Was she correct?

A No, because $2 \times \$2.25 = \$4.50$

B No, because $3 \times \$2.25 = \$6.75$

C Yes, because $\$8.00 - \$2.25 = \$5.75$

D Yes, because $3 + \$2.75 = \$5.75$

4 Gwen waits 15 minutes every day for her ride. To find out how long she waits in total for five days, Gwen multiplied 5×15. What is another way to find how long she waits for 5 days?

A $15 \div 5$

B $15 + 5$

C $15 + 15 + 15 + 15 + 15$

D $15 + 15 + 15$

Go On ➡

5 Robert is thinking of two numbers: their sum is 45 and their difference (the answer when you subtract) is 15. What are the numbers?

A   10, 15

B   15, 30

C   20, 35

D   15, 45

Questions 6–9 can be solved in more than one way.

6 Nina is 5 feet 4 inches tall. Her brother is 4 feet 6 inches tall. How much taller is Nina than her brother?

A   6 inches

B   8 inches

C   10 inches

D   12 inches

7 Letters from A to F are worth 3 points; letters from G to M are worth 4 points; letters from N to S are worth 5 points; and letters from T to Z are worth 2 points. Find the value of the word "loyalty."

A   25 points

B   22 points

C   21 points

D   20 points

8 Karl spent $16 for a special model airplane. Jeff spent half as much for a model boat. How much did they spend all together?

A $24

B $20

C $16

D $8

9 Kelly gets 5 cents for each empty bottle she returns to the supermarket. How many bottles must she return to earn $5.50?

Go On ➡

Extended Constructed Response

10 A car service charges $3.50 for the first mile and $1.50 for each additional mile.

Step A How much will a 5-mile ride cost?

_____

Step B • Use what you know about problem solving to explain why your answer is correct. Use words and/or numbers to support your explanation.

_____

_____

_____

• Suppose a classmate looked at your solution in Step A and did not understand how you found the answer. Show another way to find the answer to help the classmate understand. Explain each step using words and/or numbers.

_____

_____

_____

_____

STOP

LESSON 42

Asking Questions in Problem Solving

José wants to find out about the TV viewing habits of students in his class. Which of these questions will be the LEAST helpful?

A   How many hours of TV do you watch each day?

B   What are the three shows you watch most frequently?

C   How much did your TV cost?

D   Do you watch TV before or after you finish your homework? Do you watch during homework?

STRATEGY: **Ask yourself which of the four answers does NOT pertain to the viewing habits of the students.**

ANSWER A: The number of hours pertains to the viewing habits. The number tells us how much TV a student watches.

ANSWER B: By naming the top three shows, we get an idea of whether a student enjoys sports, situation comedies, police stories, etc.

ANSWER C: The price of a TV set has nothing to do with viewing behavior. This is the answer.

ANSWER D: When a student watches TV would be an important part of the survey.

SOLUTION: **The answer is C.**

Sample Test Questions

1 All these factors are taken into account to determine the price of a math textbook, except one. Which one?

    A the number of books to be printed

    B the number of pages

    C the ages of the authors

    D what competing textbook companies are charging

2 A television executive earns $2,000,000 per year. If the executive works 8 hours per day, 5 days per week, 50 weeks per year, about how much does the executive earn per hour?

    A $100

    B $1,000

    C $10,000

    D $20,000

3 Darren earns $18 per hour when he works. Erin makes $22 per hour when she works. What conclusion can you draw?

    A Erin earns more money per year than Darren.

    B Erin has a better education than Darren.

    C Darren earns more money per year than Erin.

    D You cannot determine who earns more per year.

4 A teacher wants to rate a student's term project in science. Which question is least important for the teacher to consider?

    A What is the quality of the written work?

    B What grade did the student get on last year's project?

    C How well did the student follow directions in preparing the project?

    D What kind of research did the student do for the project?

Go On ➡

Brief Constructed Response

5 Barry earns $950 per week at his job. Next week he will get a 5% raise.

Step A Write a question that can be answered from the information above.

_____

_____

_____

_____

Step B Use what you know about asking questions to solve problems to explain why your answer is correct. Use words and/or numbers to support your explanation.

_____

_____

_____

_____

_____

43 Representing Situations to Solve Problems

Standards 7.C.1.c, e

Putting a word problem into a mathematical form like an equation, an inequality, or a graph is called **expressing** or **representing** it. Two ways to use mathematics to represent a situation are using *figures* and using *letters*.

Example 1

What is the shape of an object whose sides contain the points (1,2), (1,0), (0,0), and (0,2) on a coordinate grid?

STRATEGY: **Draw a coordinate grid and place the points on it.**

   STEP 1: Draw the grid. It doesn't have to be perfect—a good sketch will do:

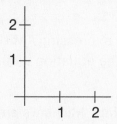

   STEP 2: Here is where you have to be careful. Place a dot on your coordinate grid for each of the four points:

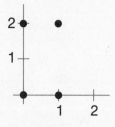

   STEP 3: Connect the four points and identify the figure:

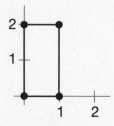

SOLUTION: **The figure is a rectangle.**

249

Example 2

Michael saved $20 more than Beverly last summer. He saved $40 per week for 8 weeks. Write an equation that can be used to find out how much money Beverly saved.

STRATEGY: **Translate the sentence logically into mathematical symbols.**

STEP 1: Compute the amount of money that Michael saved last summer.

He saved $40 per week for 8 weeks:

$40 \times 8 = 320$

He saved $320 last summer.

STEP 2: Let the letter x stand for the amount of money Beverly saved.

STEP 3: Write an equation translating the sentence: "Michael saved $20 more than Beverly last summer."

This sentence is the same as "Michael's amount is equal to $20 plus Beverly's amount."

SOLUTION: $320 = 20 + x$

NOTE: You could also think of the equation as expressing "Michael's amount minus Beverly's amount is $20." In that case, the equation would be written as $320 - x = 20$.

Or you could think of the equation as expressing "Michael's amount minus $20 is Beverly's amount." In that case, the equation would be written as $320 - 20 = x$.

There's often more than one way to write an equation.

Sample Test Questions

1 What would be the shape of an object whose corners were at the following points on a coordinate grid?

(−4,2), (−2,−2), (4,2), (2,−2)

A rectangle

B trapezoid

C square

D rhombus

2 There are 88 students in the 8th grade at South River Middle School. 22 students study French, 9 study Spanish, and 3 study Italian. Four of these students study two languages. No student takes three languages. How many students are not studying any languages?

A 48

B 50

C 54

D 58

3 At the card show, Daniel bought 3 times as many baseball cards as Sandy. Together they bought 100 cards. If s stands for the number of cards that Sandy bought, which equation could be used to determine s?

A $3s = 100$

B $\frac{3}{s} = 10$

C $s + 3s = 100$

D $s + 100 = 3s$

Go On ➡

251

Brief Constructed Response

4 A quadrilateral on a coordinate grid has four corners with coordinates (1,3), (3,0), (1,–3) and (−1,0).

Step A Name at least one special name that can be used for the quadrilateral.

_____

Step B Use what you know about representing problems to explain why your answer is correct. Use words, numbers, and/or drawings to support your explanation.

_____

_____

_____

_____

Constructed Response Questions

Brief Constructed Responses

1 A palindrome is a word, phrase, or number that reads the same forward and backward. Some examples are 23,432, noon, "Madam, I'm Adam," and 1,045,401.

Step A What are the first five palindromic numbers greater than 1,000?

_____

_____

_____

_____

Step B Explain which problem-solving strategy you used. Use words and/or numbers to explain why your answer is correct.

_____

_____

_____

_____

2 Harriet is twice as old as George. Harriet is older than 15 and younger than 20.

Step A How old could George be?

_____

Step B Use what you know about representing situations to solve problems to explain why your answer is correct. Use words and/or numbers to support your explanation.

_____

_____

_____

_____

Go On ➡

3   The number of tickets sold for Smithtown High School's basketball team games this year was 40,500. This was 10% less than a year ago.

Step A   Write a question that can be answered from the information above.

_____

_____

_____

Step B   Use what you know about asking questions to solve problems to explain why your answer is correct. Use words and/or numbers to support your explanation.

_____

_____

_____

_____

_____

Go On

Extended Constructed Response

4 Holly said that the ratio of her allowance to Rocío's allowance is the same as Rocío's allowance is to Manny's allowance. Holly's allowance is $8, and Manny's allowance is $12.50. What is Rocío's allowance?

Step A Model the problem with an equation that can be used to find Rocío's allowance.

_____

_____

Step B • Use what you know about making models to explain why your answer is correct. Use words and/or numbers to support your explanation.

_____

_____

_____

• Solve the equation to solve the problem. Explain any other strategies you used.

_____

_____

MSA
Grade 8

Practice Test

Calculator Permitted (Questions 1–41)

1 A circle has a diameter of 12 inches. Which is the best estimate of the area of the circle?

○ **A** 19 square inches

○ **B** 38 square inches

○ **C** 113 square inches

○ **D** 452 square inches

2 This scatter plot compares the height and weight of 9 elementary school students.

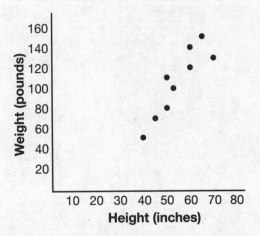

What conclusion can you draw from this scatter plot?

○ **A** As height increases, so does weight.

○ **B** As height increases, weight decreases.

○ **C** As height increases, weight remains about the same.

○ **D** There is no relationship between the two sets of data.

Go On ➡

3 What is the eighth term in this sequence?

2, 6, 18, 54,...

4 In this diagram line *a* is parallel to line *b*, and line *t* is a transversal. Which pair of angles are corresponding angles?

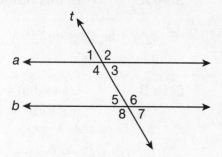

○ **A** ∠1 and ∠8

○ **B** ∠4 and ∠6

○ **C** ∠2 and ∠8

○ **D** ∠2 and ∠6

Go On ➡

5 Kyle researched the annual budget of his town and discovered that it was 28,600,000 dollars.

Step A   Write this number in scientific notation.

_____

Step B   • Use what you know about writing numbers in scientific notation to explain why your answer is correct.

_____

_____

_____

_____

• Suppose Kyle made a mistake and the budget was 10 times as great as the number he recorded. How would you have to change your answer in Step B to show the new number in scientific notation? Explain your steps.

_____

_____

_____

_____

_____

Go On ➡

6 A blueprint of a house has a scale 0.25 in. = 1 ft. How many feet long is a deck that is 3.5 inches long on the blueprint?

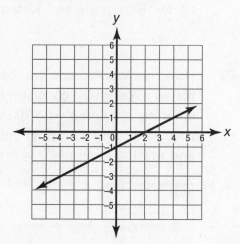

7 Which of the following best describes this graph?

○ **A** linear

○ **B** nonlinear

○ **C** both linear and nonlinear

○ **D** neither linear nor nonlinear

8 Which of the following shows 0.00074 in scientific notation?

○ **A** 7.4×10^4

○ **B** 7.4×10^5

○ **C** 7.4×10^{-4}

○ **D** 7.4×10^{-5}

9 This drawing shows how to—

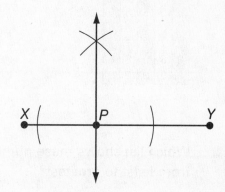

○ **A** construct a bisector of an angle.

○ **B** construct a perpendicular to a line segment through a point on the segment.

○ **C** construct a perpendicular bisector of a segment.

○ **D** construct a segment congruent to a given segment.

Go On ➡

10 What is the probability of rolling two number cubes and getting two 5s?

11 Which list shows these numbers from least to greatest?

$\frac{7}{8}$, 0.$\overline{8}$, 87.8%, 0.88

○ **A** 87.8%, $\frac{7}{8}$, 0.88, 0.$\overline{8}$

○ **B** $\frac{7}{8}$, 87.8%, 0.$\overline{8}$, 0.88

○ **C** $\frac{7}{8}$, 0.88, , 0.$\overline{8}$, 87.8%

○ **D** $\frac{7}{8}$, 87.8%, 0.88, 0.$\overline{8}$

12 This circle graph compares the amounts raised by high school students in a charity drive.

Money Raised in Charity Drive

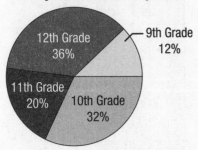

Which two grades together account for less than half the total amount raised?

○ **A** 10th grade and 11th grade

○ **B** 11th grade and 12th grade

○ **C** 9th grade and 11th grade

○ **D** 10th grade and 12th grade

13 How many outcomes are there for an experiment consisting of spinning a spinner with 10 equal sectors, rolling a number cube, and tossing a penny?

Go On ➡

262

14 Calvin can make 12 party favors per hour.

Step A Write an inequality to find the number of hours, *n*, Calvin will have to work to make 96 or more party favors.

_____

Step B Use what you know about writing inequalities for word statements to explain why your answer is correct. Use words and/or numbers to support your explanation.

_____

_____

_____

_____

_____

Go On ➡

15 Triangle *MNO* is similar to triangle *PQR*.

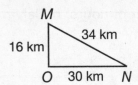

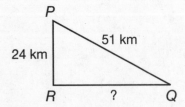

What is the length, in km, of side *RQ*?

16 A circle has a radius of 4 centimeters. Which is the best estimate of the circumference of the circle?

○ **A** 6 cm

○ **B** 13 cm

○ **C** 25 cm

○ **D** 50 cm

17 Which integer is closest to $\sqrt{52}$?

○ **A** 5

○ **B** 6

○ **C** 7

○ **D** 8

Go On ➡

18 Last year Nilda joined a mail order CD club. She paid a basic membership fee of $12.99. Each CD she bought cost $8.95. If *n* stands for the number of CDs she bought, which expression shows the total amount she spent in the CD club?

○ **A** ($12.99 + $8.95) × *n*

○ **B** $8.95*n* + $12.99

○ **C** $12.99 + $8.95 + *n*

○ **D** $12.99*n* + $8.95

19 This table shows the distance in kilometers between some towns.

	Parker	Broomfield
Aurora	3.5	4.7
Lakewood	9.3	5.9
Boulder	11.2	15.1
Littleton	17.0	21.0
Edgertown	8.4	2.2

How much farther is it, in km, from Edgertown to Parker than from Aurora to Broomfield?

Go On ➡

20 Consider regular hexagon *ABCDEF* and regular hexagon *GHIJKL*. The ratio of a side of *ABCDEF* to a side of *GHIJKL* is 3:4.

Step A   If the length of side *AB* is 9 cm, what is the length of side *GH*?

_____

Step B   • Use what you know about similar figures to explain why your answer is correct. Use words, numbers, and/or drawings to support your explanation.

_____
_____
_____
_____

   • Another regular hexagon *QRSTUV* has sides that are 4 times as long as the sides of hexagon *GHIJKL*. What is the ratio of the length of side *AB* to the length of side *QR*? Explain.

_____
_____
_____
_____
_____

Go On ➡

21 $8 - 6(27 \div 9) + 4^2 = ?$

○ **A** −2

○ **B** 6

○ **C** 14

○ **D** 22

22 In this diagram, line *g* is parallel to line *f*, and line *t* is a transversal. If the measure of ∠5 = 41°, what is the measure of ∠1? (Disregard the ° mark when gridding your answer.)

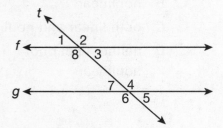

23 Shawna paid $7.40 for 4 gallons of gasoline. At that rate, how much would she pay for 6 gallons of gasoline?

○ **A** $1.85

○ **B** $11.10

○ **C** $14.80

○ **D** $22.20

Go On ➡

24 Which quadrilateral best fits this description?

It has two angles that measure 60°, two angles that measure 120°, and both pairs of opposite sides that measure 3 centimeters.

○ **A**
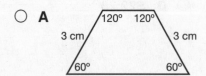

○ **B**
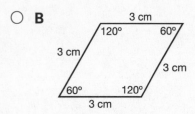

○ **C**
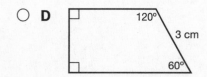

○ **D**
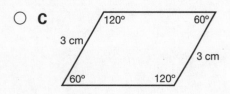

25 Which of the following best describes this graph?

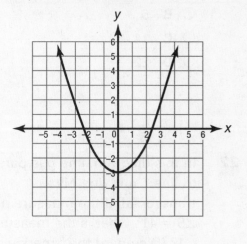

○ **A** linear

○ **B** nonlinear

○ **C** both linear and nonlinear

○ **D** neither linear nor nonlinear

Go On ➡

26 Which is the best estimate of the volume of a cylinder, in cm³, whose radius is 4 cm and whose height is 10 cm?

27 Which linear equation matches this graph?

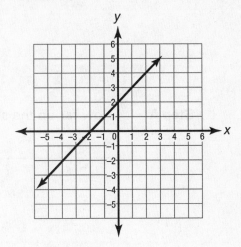

○ **A** $y = 2 - x$

○ **B** $y = x + 2$

○ **C** $y = x - 2$

○ **D** $y = 2x$

Go On ➡

28 The top of a 17-ft ladder is resting against the side of a house. The bottom of the ladder is 8 ft from the base of the house.

Step A How far up the side of the house does the ladder reach?

_____

Step B Use what you know about the sides of a right triangle to explain why your answer is correct. Use words, numbers, and/or drawings to support your explanation.

_____

_____

_____

_____

_____

Go On ➡

29   Mrs. Negron sells real estate. Recently she sold a house for $150,000. Her commission was 6% of the selling price.

Step A   How much money did Mrs. Negron earn in selling the house?

_____

Step B   • Use what you know about finding a percent of a number to explain why your answer is correct. Use words and/or numbers to support your explanation.

_____

_____

_____

• If she sells a house for more than $150,000, Mrs. Negron earns an extra 3% commission on the additional amount. What would be her total commission for selling a $175,000 house?

_____

_____

_____

_____

_____

Go On ➡

30 Solve: $6(3n - 4) - 8n = 76$

    ○ **A** 10

    ○ **B** −2

    ○ **C** −8

    ○ **D** −10

31 Which expression is the same as $(-7 \times 8) + (-7 \times 2)$?

    ○ **A** $-7 \times (8 + 2)$

    ○ **B** $-7 \times (8 \times 2)$

    ○ **C** $(-7 + 8) \times 2$

    ○ **D** $(-7 \times 8) + 2$

32 What is the area of this figure in square units?

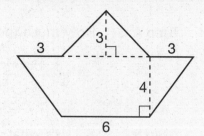

Go On ➡

33 This drawing shows how to—

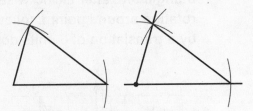

- ○ **A** construct a triangle congruent to a given triangle using the ASA relationship.
- ○ **B** construct a triangle congruent to a given triangle using the SSS relationship.
- ○ **C** construct a triangle congruent to a given triangle using the SAS relationship.
- ○ **D** construct a triangle congruent to a given triangle using the AAA relationship.

34 Identify the hypotenuse of this right triangle.

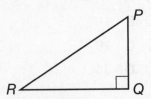

- ○ **A** side *PR*
- ○ **B** side *RQ*
- ○ **C** sides *PQ*
- ○ **D** sides *PQ* and *RQ*

35 What is the slope of this line?

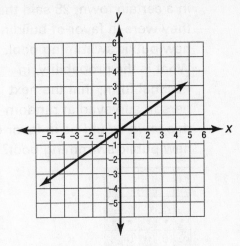

- ○ **A** $-\frac{3}{2}$
- ○ **B** $-\frac{2}{3}$
- ○ **C** $\frac{2}{3}$
- ○ **D** $\frac{3}{2}$

36 Harvey bought a stereo for $325. The sales tax in his state is 6%. How much tax did Harvey have to pay on the stereo?
(Disregard the dollar sign when gridding your answer.)

Go On ➡

273

37 In a random survey of 50 people in a certain town, 28 said that they were in favor of building a new public swimming pool. What is the probability, in decimal form, that the next person surveyed at random in this town would be in favor of a new public swimming pool?

38 What are the coordinates of triangle *JKL* after a clockwise 90° rotation around point *L* followed by a translation of 6 units down?

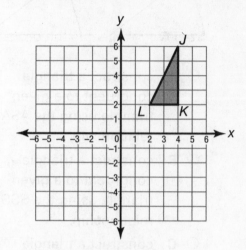

- ○ **A** (6,−6), (2,−6), (2,−4)
- ○ **B** (6,0), (2,0), (2,2)
- ○ **C** (4,0), (4,−4), (2,−4)
- ○ **D** (6,−5), (2,−5), (3,−3)

39 What is the eighth term in this sequence?

−8, −2, 4, 10,...

- ○ **A** −34
- ○ **B** 16
- ○ **C** 28
- ○ **D** 34

Go On ➡

40   The Astronomy Club at Greenville High School picks its president and vice president by random selection. Last week, the names of 15 boys and 10 girls were placed in a box. The first person selected will be president, the second will be vice president.

Step A   What is the probability that a girl will become president and a boy vice president?

_____

Step B   Use what you know about the probability of dependent events to explain why your answer is correct. Use words and/or numbers to support your explanation.

_____

_____

_____

_____

_____

Go On ➡

275

41 This data represents the numbers of cars parked in the school parking lot over the past 3 weeks:

25 28 31 35 23 27 28 19

28 35 17 18 25 22 29

Step A Draw a box-and-whisker plot of the data.

Step B • Use what you know about drawing box-and-whisker plots to explain why your answer is correct. Use words and/or numbers to support your explanation.

_____

_____

_____

_____

• Is the median a good representative of the number of cars parked over the 3-week period? Use words and/or numbers to support your explanation.

_____

_____

_____

Go On ➡

Calculator Not Permitted (Questions 42–54)

42 Find the product:

$$11 \times (-12) \times 7$$

- ○ **A** −924
- ○ **B** −30
- ○ **C** 65
- ○ **D** 924

43 Petra invested $350 at 7% simple interest for 3 years. How many dollars in interest did she earn? Use the formula $i = prt$. (Disregard the dollar sign when gridding your answer.)

44 Solve: $9d + 7 - 4d \leq 52$

- ○ **A** $d \leq 7$
- ○ **B** $d \leq 9$
- ○ **C** $d \geq 7$
- ○ **D** $d < 9$

45 What is the value of $4x - y$ when $x = -3.5$ and $y = 8$?

- ○ **A** −22
- ○ **B** −1.5
- ○ **C** 6
- ○ **D** 22

Go On ➡

46 Which circle graph displays this data?

Favorite After-School Activities

Activity	Number of Students
Band	10
Choir	21
Computer Club	14
Tutoring Club	5

○ **A** Favorite After-School Activities

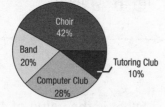

○ **B** Favorite After-School Activities

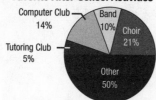

○ **C** Favorite After-School Activities

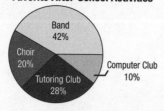

○ **D** Favorite After-School Activities

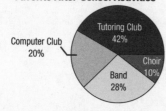

47 Find the value of n:

$$4^9 \times 4^2 = 4^n$$

○ **A** 7

○ **B** 11

○ **C** 18

○ **D** 81

48 This data represents the number of people using a public library during each hour the library was open on Thursday.

30	35	51	12	48	28
54	53	42	20	52	

Which box-and-whisker plot displays the data?

○ **A**

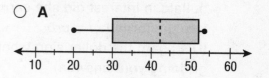

○ **B**

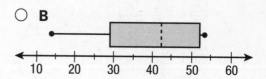

○ **C**

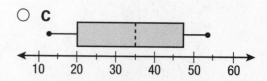

○ **D**

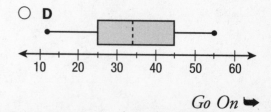

Go On ➡

278

49 Simplify by combining like terms:

$$17a + 11b - 4a + 5b$$

- ○ **A** $21a + 16b$
- ○ **B** $28ab + 1ab$
- ○ **C** $13a + 6b$
- ○ **D** $13a + 16b$

50 $\sqrt{121} = ?$

- ○ **A** 11
- ○ **B** 60.5
- ○ **C** 121
- ○ **D** 242

51 Which equation is equivalent to $9y - 3 = 276$?

- ○ **A** $9y = 273$
- ○ **B** $9y = 279$
- ○ **C** $9y = 92$
- ○ **D** $6y = 276$

52 Which inequality has this graph for its solution?

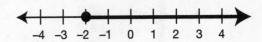

- ○ **A** $x - 6 \geq 4$
- ○ **B** $4x \leq -8$
- ○ **C** $x + 6 \geq 4$
- ○ **D** $5x \geq 10$

Go On ➡

279

53 This data represents the hourly wages and the ages of 7 people who work in the same office.

Hourly Wage	$8	$20	$14	$10	$14	$24	$30
Age	25	30	25	35	20	40	38

Which scatter plot displays the data?

○ **A**
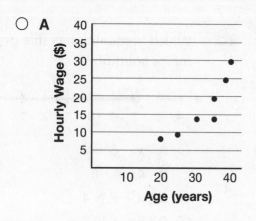

○ **C**
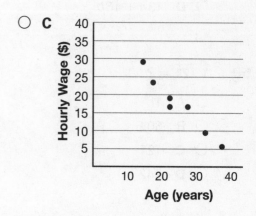

○ **B**
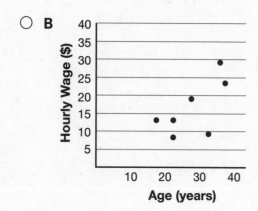

○ **D**
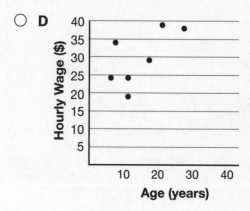

Go On ➡

54 The floor of a room has the shape of a trapezoid. The trapezoid has a height of 20 feet and bases that are 17.8 feet and 10.6 feet.

Step A What is the area of the floor? Use the formula $A = \frac{1}{2}h(b_1 + b_2)$.

_____

Step B Use what you know about applying formulas to explain why your answer is correct. Use words and/or numbers to support your explanation.

_____

_____

_____

_____

_____

STOP

NOTES

NOTES

NOTES